MW00833965

Green Thirteen

A HIWAY Book

HIWAY

Green Thirteen

Margaret
and George Ogan

HIWAY

The Westminster Press
Philadelphia

First edition

PUBLISHED BY THE WESTMINSTER PRESS®
Philadelphia, Pennsylvania

Printed in the United States of America

9 8 7 6 5 4 3 2 1

Library of Congress Cataloging in Publication Data

Ogan, Margaret Nettles.
  Green thirteen.

  SUMMARY: Jim Justin's racing career blooms and the future looks good for him until the 500 Miler at the Ontario Motor Speedway.
  [1. Automobile racing—Fiction] I. Ogan, George, joint author. II. Title.
PZ7.O3313Gt   [Fic]   77–15935
ISBN 0–664–32624–2

To Betty Baucum Jackson
and her staff
at the
Caldwell Parish Library

1

I was racing my green Triumph TR-4 roadster that Sunday afternoon on the road course at Georgetown International Speedway, running ten seconds ahead of the nearest Class D car in the race. My car was in good shape and I was having one of those afternoons when I couldn't seem to do anything wrong.

Dennis Johnson, Jr., was having a good day, too, winning the Class A race in his Jaguar Mark IV, a sports car sponsored by his father's company, Johnson Speed Components. I was cutting two-minute laps, which is fast driving in a Class D car. In his heavier and faster Jaguar, Dennis hadn't lapped me yet.

I was coming down the mile-long straight past the pits and grandstand. The sharp left, only slightly banked turn at the end of that straight was coming up. A glance in the rearview told me Dennis had his Jag directly behind my TR-4.

I'd been using a high line into this turn all afternoon, sweeping down across it, but Dennis was closing on my rear bumper fast. My braking point was coming up. I pointed down the track, signaling Dennis to go under me if he had to pass here.

I braked, popped the clutch, shifted down, and the nose of the heavy Jag slammed into the tail of my featherweight TR-4. The impact snapped my head back and lifted my car, bunting it over the guardrail.

One second my tires were scrubbing the track, the next I was airborne, pointing directly at a six-foot cyclone fence. When you've been shunted that badly, and aren't expecting it, there isn't time to get scared. There isn't time for prayer. You just hang on, knowing Death has stopped looking over your shoulder and is staring you in the face.

My car's front end dropped, front wheels hitting a shallow drainage ditch. That flipped the TR-4 end over end, ripping through the fence.

My helmet hit the roll bar and split like an egg. My left foot was trapped between the brake pedal and the accelerator. When my helmet split, a bolt of lightning shot through my head. My left ankle and knee were a red blaze of pain, but only for a second.

I spun down and down into a deep, dark well.

When you've been unconscious, you hear before you can see, or even feel. "We have to take him into surgery now, Mrs. Justin." Dr. Grant was speaking. "It was a bad accident, but J.J. is a tough young man. He'll be all right."

"Thank God!" Mother was standing close to me. Cool fingers brushed my forehead, then clutched my hand. "James? Speak to me."

Her face, staring down into mine, was only a pale

8

blur. But when Mother uses that tone of voice to say, "James?" . . . well, you answer.

"Hi, Mom," I managed to say. Her face was clearer now. She had been crying. "Don't do that," I said. "What time is it?"

"Seven o'clock."

"You're going to be late to work."

"I am at work," she said. "You're in Columbia Hospital."

"How did I get here?" I had no memory of the accident.

"In an ambulance," Dr. Grant said, "and now let's get this boy into surgery."

A needle pricked my arm.

Mother is night supervisor of nurses at the Columbia Hospital. I expected her to be there when I came out of never-never land, but Voncil Shakne was standing beside my bed. Voncil is a nurse and one of my cousins. She's my prettiest cousin and the most shapely.

Voncil frowned as she scribbled something on a clipboard tied to the foot of my bed. A bottle of yellowish liquid was on a rack beside my bed with a clear plastic tube thrust into my arm.

Voncil finished scribbling. When she reached for my pulse, she saw that my eyes were open, and said, "Welcome back, J.J. Did you have a nice nap?"

"I guess so. How am I doing?" I was now beginning to remember the accident.

"You're alive," Voncil said. "That's all Dr. Grant

allows us to tell postoperative patients."

There was another bed in the room and whoever was in it spoke up.

"You're a mess." Dennis Johnson would have to be my roommate. "Your face looks like raw hamburger, you have a busted ankle, you dislocated your knee, and all you have going for you is no concussion. You have a thick skull."

I groaned. "What else is new?"

"Your little car burned up and you owe Georgetown International for a hole in their new fence."

"Shut up, Dennis," Voncil snapped at him.

"One thing, J.J. You did signal you were going down to let me through, didn't you?"

"No. What I signaled . . ." I was too tired to argue the point. "Why are you here?"

"Dennis is a hero." Voncil was sarcastic. "After trying to kill you he crawled through that hole in the fence to pull you from your burning car. He's also striking to be the worst patient we've ever had."

"Don't believe her," Dennis said. "I'm an angel with folded wings."

My left leg was in traction, but I squirmed enough to see Dennis. He was sitting up with both arms bandaged to the elbows and gauze mitts on his hands.

"What happened to you?" I asked.

"These?" Dennis moved his arms and winced. "Miss Shakne just told you that I pulled you out of your car. If I'd known I was going to fry my hands and arms, I would have left you in it."

"Thanks a lot. I hope you get a Purple Heart. I'd

like to be the one to pin it on you."

"Now both of you shut up," Voncil said.

"Where's my mother?" I asked.

"Dr. Grant sent her home after she bandaged up Dennis," Voncil told me. "Your arrival here didn't exactly make her night."

"Hey, was that your mother?" Dennis asked. "She was wonderful. Didn't say a damn thing about me busting you up. Your father sure picked himself a wife."

"Dennis Johnson . . ." Anger flags flared in Voncil's cheeks.

"Hey, it's all right, cool it," I told her. "My father was killed on the river when I was seven," I explained to Dennis.

"Bite my tongue," Dennis muttered. "Sorry about that. We lost our mother to cancer six years ago."

"Now that you two half-orphans know each other," Voncil said, "shut up and go to sleep. If you don't, I'll come back with a dull needle."

Dennis whistled softly when Voncil left. "Now I could really go overboard for that girl," he said. "She has what I call genuine female packaging. Do you know her, J.J.?"

"Yes, as a matter of fact. She's my cousin."

Dennis slumped down in his bed. "Bite my tongue again."

I'm James Justin III, twenty-two, hometown: Columbia, Louisiana. Columbia is on the Ouachita River, and if you want to pronounce that so natives

11

don't laugh you out of town, say "Wash-i-taw."

Until my TR-4 was tail ended by the Johnson Jaguar, I worked six days on an offshore oil drilling rig, with six days off to rest.

Columbia is in northern Louisiana near Monroe. My car was transportation to Gilmore Oil Company's helicopter pad in Morgan City, as well as my weekend race car. Painted bright green, it was numbered 13 when I bought it off a used car lot in Monroe. The former owner traded it for a Porsche so he could go Class A racing.

I won the first race I entered driving my green car and changed neither the color nor the number for two reasons.

Race drivers are superstitious and consider a green car unlucky, and when it's numbered 13, sheer disaster! So I seldom had trouble finding driving room on the track. My TR-4 was called "that jinx car" and other drivers stayed out of my way.

My second reason for not repainting or renumbering the car was money. I had rebuilt the race-tired engine. I had all the previous owners' dings and dents ironed out of the sheet metal. I also bought a set of soft-rubber racing slicks. By then my car budget was shot.

Racing was my hobby. It's expensive but it blew away the frustrations of spending six days 150 miles out in the Gulf of Mexico, dancing the monkey boards and rubbing elbows with Cajuns and Rednecks. We had a good crew on Gilmore's platform 36, but six 24-hour days of all-male company is a little much.

My father, James Justin II, was a husky six-footer with black hair and slate-gray eyes, the best towboat skipper on the Ouachita or the Mississippi. He owned his own boat, the *Francine,* named after my mother. I don't remember him very well. He was seldom off the river, and at seven you soon get used to not having a father. You shut memories of him out of your mind.

I know what he was like because Mother says I'm a dead-ringer for him in size, looks, and build.

My grandfather, James Justin I, earned a chest full of medals before he was killed on the Anzio Beachhead during World War II. He was a full colonel at the time and was awarded the Medal of Honor posthumously.

For rescuing one of his crew from a damaged barge before he suffocated from ammonia fumes, my father got a bronze Carnegie Medal. It hangs under the crucifix on one wall of my mother's bedroom.

Mother is a small woman from Morgan City in southern Louisiana with more than a quart of French blood in her veins. Her father was a shrimper with his own boat and didn't quite beat Hurricane Camille into port.

With insurance money, after my father died, Mother put herself through the nursing school over at Northeastern University in Monroe. She was only seventeen when I was born, twenty-four when my father was killed.

With dark eyes and olive complexion and a dazzling smile, Mother is beautiful, but it's not skin-deep beauty. Being a devout Catholic may have helped her accept my father's death, leaving her with a lunk of a kid to raise, but Mother has a hard core. She doesn't know the word "defeat." Mix that with compassion for anyone sick or injured and you have quite a woman.

The morning after my left ankle was set and put in a cast, and my knee relocated, with surgery to repair torn cartilages, the first question I asked my mother when she came to see Dennis and me was, "When can I get out of here?"

"It took you only five seconds to get in here," Mother said, "but the day of miracles has passed. You'll have to wait until Dr. Grant decides to let you go. How was your breakfast?"

Dennis Johnson, Sr., arrived during morning visiting hours. When the blocky man in rumpled khakis came into the room, with gray streaks in his brown hair, I thought he'd come to fix the plumbing. He stopped at the foot of my bed. Brown eyes studied me.

"How are you making it, son?" he asked. "I'm the father of the lead-footed Jaguar driver in that other bed."

"I've felt better," I said, "but never more lucky, Mr. Johnson."

14

"Yeah. I've seen you win some tough ones. How are you fixed for hospital insurance?"

"On the job, okay. Off the job, racing, I just don't know."

"Don't worry about it," Mr. Johnson said. He pulled up a chair to talk with Dennis. "Our junkyard has your Jaguar," he told Dennis.

"I blew it, didn't I?" Dennis groaned.

"The race stewards seem to think it was an unavoidable accident," Mr. Johnson said. "Of course, pulling J.J. out of his car may have influenced their judgment, but both of you are in the clear."

"I was trying to pass. It was my fault," Dennis said. "That sure makes me feel rotten."

"Oh, come on, knock it off, Dennis," I said. "Go racing and you have to expect a shunt once in a while. It sends the crowd home happy."

Dennis raised on one elbow. "You're sure not much to look at right now, J.J.," he said, "but do you want to know something?"

"I can hardly wait."

"You grow on a guy even if you do snore."

"Well, thanks, I think."

Dennis grinned. "But then, so do warts."

Mr. Johnson chuckled and got up to leave. "Denise sends her best," he told Dennis. "Now I have to get back to work. Don't be too hard on the nurses, fellows. By the way, Dennis, I almost forgot. We have a deal with Pontiac for Firebirds to race the All-American Cup series."

"Hey, that's great news!" Dennis said. "Do I get to drive one?"

"Not until your driving improves." Mr. Johnson winked at me and was gone.

The All-American Cup series would be a series of ten races for fat purses in American-made sports cars. The racers would be divided into two-car teams. The team with the most points at the end of the series would receive a Gold Cup plus $350,000. The individual driver with the most points would get $150,000.

"You have as much chance to make the All-Am races, Dennis," I told him, "as you have of making a major-league ball club. Why not try out for the Mets or Yankees instead?"

"Because I can't hit a baseball for swatting flies," he said, grinning. Dennis had the same stubborn jawline as his father, but dark hair like mine. His regular features have, unlike mine, a handsome cast. "Make nice to me, J.J. I'll try to get you a ride in the other team car."

"You are a dreamer, friend," I said. "Your father wants name drivers in those cars, not a couple of sports car buffs like you and me."

"Bill Kelly is going to prepare the cars. You know who he is, don't you?"

"Sure, I know about Kelly."

Bill Kelly raced the NASCAR circuit until an accident at Daytona crippled him. He has stayed with auto racing as a master mechanic. He is a sought-after man to prepare NASCAR and USAC stock cars, and I was surprised Mr. Johnson had managed to hire him. He was certainly all-out to track a pair of winning cars.

"Your father does things right," I said.

Dennis laughed. "That's how he got rich. Dad goes the limit or not at all. Seriously, J.J., with Kelly preparing those cars, I think we could win some races. You know how many drivers never make it because they can't get the right car."

"I know," I said. "The woods are full of them. A stroker written off as a never-was gets in the right car and he's off and winning. But Detroit isn't going to let a couple of nameless drivers like us get in the game, and you know it."

My accident insurance didn't cover me while racing. Dr. Grant owns Columbia Hospital, and wouldn't have pushed Mother and me hard to pay our bill, which was more than two thousand dollars when I finally got out, but Mr. Johnson was stubborn about picking up the tab.

I overheard him and Mother discussing the matter in the corridor outside my room. Dennis had already gone home.

"We're not going to have any nonsense, Mrs. Justin," Mr. Johnson told Mother. "If my son hadn't wrecked his car, J.J. wouldn't be in here and off work."

"We don't accept charity," Mother said.

"Be damned to that! Don't insult me with that word again. I've worked hard to afford something like this."

I expected Mother's French blood to come to a boil, but all she said was, "All right, Mr. Johnson, but J.J. and I intend to pay you back."

"With interest, I suppose?" Mr. Johnson chuckled. "Do that," he said, "and I'll spend it all on liquor and wild women. You wouldn't want to be my ruination, would you?"

Before I went home, my Gilmore supervisor offered me a job on an offshore exploratory well in the South China Sea, near Singapore. If I took the job, I'd be gone two years.

Mr. Johnson came to the hospital with a job offer too. "Dennis is laying out of Tulane's premed school next semester," he told me, "to work on our All-Am racers and maybe test drive them. I don't entirely approve, but Dennis is twenty-one." This was the middle of January, and a rainy day. "I understand you're a good engine man, J.J. Would you come to work for me? Kelly can use you."

"Johnsonville is closer to home than the Far East," I said, "and I don't like rice curry. You've got yourself a hand, Mr. Johnson, as soon as I'm on my feet."

2

I reported for work early in February at the Johnson Speed Components plant over in Johnsonville, which is forty miles from Columbia. When I'd filled out the required forms I expected to be sent to some remote corner of the six-acre Johnson main plant.

I was routed, instead, to a cement-block building separate from the main plant. It was a windowless building with air conditioning, designed, built, and equipped for one purpose—to prepare cars to race. The building alone must have cost more than fifty thousand dollars.

Mr. Johnson was going to race his Firebirds against Detroit-backed teams, with the cream of race drivers in their cars.

To win or even place in that kind of competition costs money. Mr. Johnson, I realized when I stepped into that shop, was willing to pay the price. In a pair of greasy coveralls he was on a crawler working under one of the cars.

"You're half an hour late, Justin," was Bill Kelly's welcome. "We punch in here at eight and I don't mean five minutes after, much less thirty."

Kelly eased his crippled right leg with a cane. A livid burn scar covered most of his left cheek. He was a tall, spare man with brush-cut red hair, a beak of a nose, down-turned mouth, and startling dark-blue eyes enmeshed with squint wrinkles.

"I had to make out some forms," I said.

"You should have allowed time for that," Kelly pointed out. "How's your leg?"

"It's okay, thanks."

"Count yourself lucky. I wish I could say the same. Now go over there to the solvent barrel and help Dee wash parts until I find something else for you to do."

Mr. Johnson pushed himself out from under the Firebird. "That will do it, Bill," he said, then saw me. "Good to see you, J.J."

Dennis waved a wrench at me from the other side of the shop. "You've come to the right place if you're looking for work," he said.

Kelly pointed with his cane. "The solvent barrel is over there."

It was half of a steel drum with four pipe legs welded to it. A slender kid in white coveralls and beaked painter's cap was busy washing parts.

"Welcome to the Mr. Clean detail," he said, and this kid had a soprano voice that could have gotten him into the Vienna Boys Choir. "Pick a part, any part, from the bench on our left, J.J. Bathe it in this gunk, wipe it clean, and put it over here on this bench. Simple, no? Boring, yes."

The kid pushed back his cap to give me an imp

grin, and I discovered Dee was a girl. There was a smear of oil on her pert nose. "Because I love cars I asked Daddy if I could help," she said, "and look what they have me doing. I could have stayed home and helped Mrs. Keller with the dishes instead." She wiped a small hand on the seat of her coveralls for me to shake. "I'm Denise Johnson, Dennis' kid sister."

Dee was sixteen, a small and dainty replica of Dennis.

"Keep working over there, you two," Kelly growled at us. "You're not on break."

"Yes, sir!" Dee jerked her cap down and saluted. "That man has more bark than a tree," she confided to me, "but, inside? A marshmallow! Just the same, we'd better get cracking. If you'll wash, I'll wipe."

"I'll wash," I said, and that's what I did the rest of my first day on the job.

Mr. Johnson decided our team color would be green to advertise the Johnson Green Front accessory stores, over the objections of superstitious Kelly, and further confounded Kelly by numbering one car 13 and the other 31.

March 1 was the target date to have the cars ready for test driving. The All-Am opener would be March 15 on the road track at Georgetown International, a 250-mile race.

The Sports Car Association of America (SCAA) would be sponsoring the races, with Detroit and accessory manufacturers putting up the purses. The basic idea was to wean American sports car buyers away from foreign machinery. Why not win in a Firebird instead of a Ferrari?

Manufacturers also claimed that the series, by selling more domestic cars, would help balance foreign exchange. Kelly had a cynical view about that.

"You might as well try to bail out a battleship with a tin cup," he said. "Leave it to them Detroit moguls to wrap themselves in the American flag. They'll want our exhausts tuned to play 'The Star-spangled Banner.'"

Mr. Johnson got a chuckle out of that Kelly comment. "Kelly started life as a Georgia dirt farmer," he told Dennis and me, "and he's never shaken all the red clay off his boots. No farmer ever trusts a city-bred mogul."

As I got to know Kelly better, I realized he had a split-view attitude toward Detroit. He was fascinated by the genius of Detroit's car and engine designers, but thumbs-down on Detroit executives.

"Them button-down-collar guys with a crease in their pants hurt my butt," he would say. "They got dollar signs instead of eyeballs."

Kelly lavished all his love and affection on our Green Birds. Speed with driver safety was his concern.

We mounted dual 4-barrel carburetors to feed alcohol-cooled gasoline (methanol) into the 455-cubic-inch displacement Firebird engines. Ports were relieved and cylinders punched out. It might say 455 cc on the hood, but there was a lot more displacement under that hood.

Special hood air scoops were mounted to help cool the engines. An oil-cooling radiator was installed and larger oil sumps. The crankshafts, cams, pistons, and connecting rods were perfectly balanced. Air scoops to cool the brakes were installed.

Driver safety came next. Interiors of the cars were stripped and a bucket seat mounted inside a roll cage. Car frames were strengthened. Heavier steering components, manufactured in the Johnson factory, ruled óut steering failure at high speed.

Wide-rim, lighter, and stronger racing wheels replaced the cars' stock wheels. Steel beams were welded inside the door panels. The doors were welded shut. You squirmed through a window to get into the car.

A steel beam over the engine, under the hood, kept the mill out of the driver's lap in case of a grinding head-on crash. Bumpers were welded to the fenders. Steel mesh protected the radiators from track debris.

Green Bird 13 and Green Bird 31 were beautiful to see when the sun rose March 1 and they were in the pit and garage area at Georgetown International.

"J.J., let's have at 'em!" If he had been a child, Dennis would have jumped up and down with excitement. "You beautiful cars."

I stared down the track to the spot where I'd cleared the guardrail in my late TR-4. Fear was like a cold stone in my gut. I had worked beside Kelly on the engines in these cars. I knew how much raw power was leashed under those hoods. My TR-4 was a roller skate in comparison.

Dennis, I knew from working with him, could find the starter button, the clutch, shift the five-speed Hurst gearbox, and step on the accelerator.

Kelly had predicted, "That boy will be another car-breaker." He cited the names of some top drivers who couldn't tell the carburetor from the alternator. "He'll flog a car until the engine lunches."

Kelly now watched me for a moment, as if trying to read my thoughts. Then he nodded as if the expression on my face told him what he wanted to know.

Kelly turned to Dennis. "Buster, if you so much as scratch one of my cars while we're testing, I'm going to ram it. That's a promise, and you ain't going to like *where* I ram it."

Dee and Mr. Johnson were there. She giggled, Mr. Johnson chuckled, and Kelly blushed.

"Hey, Kelly, take it easy," Dennis said. "You can trust me. I've handled hot cars before. I've won a few races, as a matter of fact."

"Listen to me good," Kelly told Dennis. "We have more horsepower under these hoods than you've ever tried to handle. One simple mistake and you're dead. Think about it." Kelly turned to me. "Take us around, J.J. I want to get the feel of Green Bird 13."

When Kelly was aboard and squatting beside my bucket seat, wearing Dennis' helmet and face shield

24

while he gripped the roll cage, I fired up the car and let it idle for a minute. I spun rear wheels going down pit alley, but Kelly didn't comment.

Head cocked, he was listening to the engine's beat.

I speeded down the long front straight, judging by engine sound when it was time to run up through the gears. I geared down, braked, and was through the first left turn and into the esses. I almost lost Green Bird 13 when the rear end began to swing, but I corrected in time with a touch of brakes.

"Sorry about that." I had to yell for Kelly to hear me over the roar of the unmuffled engine.

"Wasn't your fault," Kelly yelled back. "The chassis ain't tuned right yet."

We were through the sweeper into the long back straight. "Let her go," Kelly yelled.

I watched the tachometer needle nudge 7500 rpms and the red line there. Speed was shoving me back in the bucket seat.

Near the end of that straight is a chicane. This is roughly an S-turn with little or no camber, or bank. It's there to keep speed-happy drivers from getting into the 180-degree hairpin turn so fast they leave the track.

I burned brakes and geared down but was still going too fast when I tooled through the chicane. I was on the grass, back on the track, in a skid, on the grass again, finally back safely on the track.

"Holy jeez!" Kelly let out his breath in a whistling sigh. "Damn it, man."

"Scared me too," I admitted.

25

I took it easy through the hairpin, barely scrubbing my tires. I used to broadside through this one in my TR-4. Coming off the high-banked turn back into the main straight, I asked, "Around again, Kelly?"

He stabbed a finger at pit alley. "No. Take her in, J.J. One lap with you will hold me for a week. A strange car and the guy tries to beat the track's record," he muttered to himself. "Race drivers!"

When we'd shut it down and were out of the car I said, "Kelly, you hurt my feelings."

I was only half-kidding.

Kelly grimaced, flexing the cramps out of his hands. He'd really had a tight grip on that roll cage. "You ain't too bad out there, J.J.," he said. "It just scares the hell out of one race driver to ride with another. When you try it you'll see what I mean."

Mr. Johnson had had long phone conversations with Pontiac's racing division, but no drivers for the Green Birds had been announced yet.

Chevrolet would track a Camaro 307 and a Monte Carlo 350 for the All-Am series. Ace Allen would race the Camaro and Walt Fischer would drive the Monte Carlo. Both were NASCAR veterans with impressive wins.

Ford had prepared a Mustang 302 and a Cougar 351 for the series. Neal Hutchinson was to drive the Mustang and Bud Gowanus was to race the Cougar.

Two of Oldsmobile's Cutlass S sports coupes would be racing. Bob Frazier would pilot one of these cars. His older brother, Chet Frazier, would take the other. Both Fraziers were USAC drivers.

Gus Enright would drive one Dodge Challenger 318. Phil Spell would race another.

Mark Owens, heir to the Owens Leathercraft fortune, was preparing two Plymouth 318 Barracudas for the series. Bruce Adams would be his teammate.

This made up a field of twelve cars.

The point system for the series would be as follows:

> First 10
> Second 8
> Third 6
> Fourth 4

Any driver who finished a race, but didn't place, would be awarded one point.

After the Georgetown 250 on March 15 there would be, during April, a 400-mile race at Texas International Speedway and a 300-miler at Watkins Glen, New York.

The 350-mile Road Atlanta race would be held during May, with the 400-mile Road America race scheduled for June. Also in June there would be a 200-mile race on the Mid-Ohio Sports Car course.

During July there would be a 350-mile race at Dallas International and a 250-miler on Donnybrooke Speedway.

In August would be the series windup with a 250-mile race at Laguna Seca in California and the finale, a 500-miler at Riverside International or Ontario Motor Speedway.

There would be 3250 miles of racing.

At Kelly's suggestion, Mr. Johnson hired the Holcombe pit crew to service the Green Birds during pit stops. "They're expensive," Kelly admitted, "but Joe and his boys are the best."

Mr. Johnson had an unusual arrangement with Pontiac's racing division. They had agreed to furnish cars and engines. Mr. Johnson was to prepare the cars to race at his own expense. This way, Mr. Johnson was a semi-independent, like Mark Owens, and had control of his racing team.

Mr. Johnson agreed to consult with Pontiac but insisted on picking his own drivers.

There was an escape clause in the contract that said either party to it could terminate the arrangement at any time during the series. Winning races in the Green Birds was essential. Otherwise, Pontiac would enter factory-prepared cars with factory-picked drivers, and Mr. Johnson would be on his own.

Test driving is no cinch. The first ten days in March, with the sun shining or the sky spitting rain, Dennis and I wheeled the Green Birds around the track from dawn until dusk while Kelly made engine and chassis changes.

The steering wheels blistered our hands. Our shoulders and backs ached. Our rumps got numb. I spent my sleeping hours dream-driving, and Dennis complained about the same thing.

Mother got worried. "James, you're going to have to rest," she told me at breakfast one morning. "You come home almost too tired to undress for bed. If you keep on test driving those stupid cars, you'll go to sleep at the wheel and have an accident."

"Just one more day of it," I said. "Then I'll sleep for a week, beginning tonight."

"You went to sleep during Mass last Sunday," Mother said.

"No kidding? Father Ryan must have loved that. What was his homily about?"

"We had two emergencies at the hospital last Saturday night," Mother said and smiled. "I'm afraid I slept through it too."

When I reported for work that day, Kelly said we were finished with test driving. "The cars are ready to race now," he told us. "In ten minutes Mr. Johnson wants to see us in his office. Grab yourselves a cup of coffee, but let's not keep him waiting."

Sitting on a workbench, drinking coffee, I asked Dennis, "Do we get fired now?"

"It beats me," Dennis said. "At least we're off the hook as test drivers. We could apply up in Detroit and probably get jobs, but I'll stick with medicine."

"Maybe I can still go to Singapore."

"You might like it," Dennis said.

"In the South China Sea or out in the gulf, a drilling platform is a drilling platform. Good enough pay, and the food isn't too bad, but you work your tail off."

"Dad might want to keep us on the payroll as relief drivers," Dennis said. "We've turned some pretty fast laps in the Green Birds."

"If he does that," I said, "we'll get to watch a lot of races. Do you have any idea who's going to drive the cars?"

Dennis shook his head. "My father hasn't said. He's been hassling with Detroit about it."

"Time to go," Kelly told us.

Mr. Johnson looked tired. "Find chairs and use them," he told the three of us. "We have a matter to discuss."

When we were seated Mr. Johnson spoke to Kelly. "Have you changed your mind?"

"No, sir, I haven't," Kelly said. "I still feel the same way about it."

"Well, then that's that." Mr. Johnson paused. "J.J., Dennis, would you like to drive our Green Birds in the All-Am series? Kelly thinks you two can do the job for us."

3

Dennis and I were stunned. From Class D sports car racing, or even Class A, moving up to go with professionals is quite a jump.

"You fellows know the cars," Kelly said, "and what they'll do. By this time you're familiar enough with the Georgetown road circuit to drive it blindfolded. My money says you're ready to hack it."

"I don't know," Dennis said. "What do you think, J.J.?"

"I'm thinking," I told him.

"You'll be going with men who would run over their grandmother to win a race," Kelly said, "but you're ready to take them on."

"What if we can't cut it?" I asked Mr. Johnson. "You've invested a lot of money."

"I'll have made another mistake, that's all," Mr. Johnson told me. "It won't be my first mistake that cost money, nor my last. Why don't you just give it a try?"

We did know the cars, and we did know the track. I wanted to know if Dennis and I were as good as Kelly thought. He had done enough racing, and seen

31

enough drivers in action, to know what he was talking about.

"I'd like to give it a try," I told Kelly and Mr. Johnson.

Dennis regarded me thoughtfully, then said, "Count me in. Maybe we can do it."

This was Wednesday morning. Qualifying trials would be Saturday. The race would get off the starting grid early Sunday afternoon.

"J.J., check with your mother, but we'd like you to stay with us until after the race. You need a chance to rest and relax," Mr. Johnson said. "By the way, you'll be entitled to twenty-five percent of any money you win, and all your expenses will be paid, of course."

"That sounds good," I said, "and I accept your invitation. Mother was on me just this morning about getting some rest."

Johnsonville is named for the Johnson Plantation that Union troops burned to the ground during the Civil War. After that war, the Johnsons who came home became dirt-poor farmers. They weren't doing much better until Dennis Johnson, Sr., expanded a truck and tractor repair shop into a multi-million-dollar enterprise. He not only makes parts for Detroit manufacturers but also owns more than a hundred Johnson Green Front stores that sell speed accessories.

The Johnson estate covers part of the old plantation. From the road it looks like a modest affair, with a split-level ranch-type home made of red brick with white shutters. Behind the house, however, there is an Olympic-size swimming pool with a barbecue pit, a four-car garage with a lift so Mr. Johnson can service his own cars—two Lincolns, a Cadillac, and a Mercedes.

There is also a king-size, modern barn for riding horses and Black Angus cattle. Most of the 360-acre estate is pasture.

Over the garage are living quarters for Mr. and Mrs. Keller. Mr. Keller takes care of the cattle. Mrs. Keller is Mr. Johnson's housekeeper since Mrs. Johnson died.

"This estate is really something," I said when Dennis and Dee had shown me around.

Dee, in tan jodhpurs and a white sweater, had been exercising her mare that morning. We were back in the house. "It's an empty something with Mother gone," she said. "I wish you could have known her. Mother was a very special person."

"Why don't you take J.J. for a swim, Dee?" Dennis said. "You need one yourself. In those clothes you smell like a horse."

"I haven't any trunks," I said.

"I'll lend you a pair of mine," Dennis told me. "You're bigger than I am, so they'll be a tight fit, but they ought to do."

"Dennis, what brand of shaving lotion are you using these days?" Dee asked in a sweet voice.

"Do you like it?" He told her the brand.

"Change to something else," Dee said. "You smell

33

like . . . well, being a properly raised young woman, I won't get specific, but that is what you smell like. Change your brand. See you in the pool," Dee told me, and scampered upstairs.

Dennis rubbed his cheek and sniffed his fingers. "I have yet to get in the last word with that girl," he told me.

"I'll bet nobody does," I said. "Come to notice, you do smell pretty."

"To you, too? I guess I'd better change to X brand."

Saturday morning the Georgetown pit and garage area buzzed with activity. Kelly introduced Dennis and me to a slightly built, brown-skinned young mechanic.

"This is Joe Holcombe," he said. "Joe, our drivers, Dennis and J.J. You do the honors with your crew."

Joe grinned. "My pleasure."

A stocky Mexican named Pablo and a towering blond, Olaf Gutenborg, would be changing wheels during pit stops.

Jerry Bryan was our spotter and windshield man, slender, with dark, curly hair. Jerry would stand where we were supposed to stop. He had to be a fast scrambler if either of us came in too fast and overshot.

Sam Sanford, an older black man, was bald and walked with a decided limp. His job was to manhandle ten-gallon fuel cans and pour methanol into our tanks. That's dangerous. If fuel is spilled on a hot pipe, the car can explode.

Billy Welch, a small man with a wizened face, who had once been a jockey, would be adding oil during pit stops and handing Kelly and Joe any tools they needed to work on the engines.

When we'd met his crew, Joe said, "We'll get you out fast tomorrow, fellows." He spoke in a soft voice. "All you have to do is stay on the black part of the track and win. I think we've got the cars to do it."

Ace Allen qualified his Camaro at 143 mph while his partner, Walt Fischer, brought his Monte Carlo around at an average speed of 142.

"We've got fast company," I told Dennis.

My best lap, testing, had been 140. Dennis' was 139.

"I guess we'd better believe it," he said.

All lap speeds were in the 140 to 143 range until Mark Owens took his Barracuda out.

Kelly joined Dennis and me on the pit wall. "Watch this," he said. "Mark is as smooth a driver as you'll ever see, but that snub-nosed, sandy-haired kid likes to break records."

Kelly knew what he was talking about. The track record for qualifying was 146. Mark's speed was 148. Yet he had done it without seeming to try.

I drove my speed trial after Mark left the track. I went deep into the turns before shifting down and squeezing brakes. I wound it up down the back straight but whipped through the chicane, drifted across the hairpin with all four wheels locked up, and boomed out of the sweeper into the main straight.

Turning a slow lap to cool out Green Bird 13, I knew I'd been quicker than ever before.

On the board opposite my name it said, 147. Kelly slapped my shoulder when I was out of the car. "You and Mark should make a race out of it tomorrow, J.J."

Dennis lapped at 142. "I tried not to push the car too hard," he apologized to Kelly. "I'll be quicker tomorrow."

The cars Sunday would start in rows of two. My speed put me in the front rank, outside Mark Owens' Barracuda. Dennis was back in the field two rows.

There was a drivers' meeting after the last car had been qualified. The idea of qualifying trials is to locate the fastest cars up front on the grid, a safety measure. During those dangerous early laps, before a race settles down, stewards don't want fast cars weaving up through the field.

Rod McCune was head steward for this race. He'd black-flagged me off the track during one Class D race, claiming I was reckless.

We had had words about that. McCune, in my opinion, was a nitpicker, and officious. When we gathered for the meeting, however, the guy was nervous and awed by the driving talent he faced. He was used to dealing with weekend amateur racers with whom his word was law.

He stumbled through the usual patter about watching for flag signals at the corners and keeping it safe, then said, "Do any of you have suggestions?"

Bud Gowanus stood up. He was a portly man with a bullet head that he shaved. "We got a pair of rookie drivers starting tomorrow." Bud's voice was nasal and had a twang I couldn't quite identify. "Any rookie can qualify fast, then get squirrelly during a race. Justin? Is that your name?" Bud looked directly at me.

"It says so on the car I race," I told him.

Bud ignored my sarcasm. "You're Johnson, of course," he said to Dennis. "Nothing personal, you understand, but I think you and Justin should start at the tail end of the field. You might get hurt up front, or one of us might."

"Now wait just a damned minute." I was on my feet.

"Sit down." Mark Owens, sitting behind me, put his hand on my shoulder until I was seated. He stayed on his feet. "I've seen these so-called rookies drive, Mr. McCune," Mark said. "Both have earned their position on the starting grid. I know some drivers here agree with Bud, but I'm one who doesn't. Move Johnson and Justin back and you can put me behind them."

"Damn it, Mark . . ." Bud began, then stopped.

Phil Spell stood up. He was a lanky, older driver with a New England accent. "Why don't you put it to a vote, McCune?" Phil said. "Let's find out if we have any sportsmen here, or just a bunch of ignorant car aimers. Move those kids, you can move me back too."

"All I was suggesting . . ." Bud began, and again stopped, getting red in the face. "All right, to hell with it."

37

"What will it be, Mr. Steward?" Mark asked.

McCune cleared his throat uncomfortably. "The starting order as determined by qualifying times stands," he said.

Phil patted a yawn. "I'm buying if anyone wants a drink," he said, then grinned. "That also includes you, Bud."

That ended the drivers' meeting.

"I'll have an eye on you tomorrow, Justin," McCune said before I left. "You, too, Johnson."

"Thanks for caring," I told him. "We'll see you around."

I hurried Dennis away before he could sound off.

Sunday afternoon we turned a lap behind a pace car before the race was flagged off. I was shaking with a stomach full of butterflies. All I could think of was that I might stall Green Bird 13 before the first corner, in which case the whole field would run over me. I glanced over at Mark Owens.

He was driving in a slouch, chewing gum, with a pleasant expression on his tanned face. The guy looked as if he was out for a Sunday afternoon spin. I had caught his eye. Mark grinned at me.

That was Mark's last friendly gesture that afternoon. When the flag dropped, his Barracuda streaked away, then nearly cut me off when he took it up into a higher groove.

It was heavy traffic with that sharp left coming up. I lifted my foot. I couldn't see how all of us could make that turn. Green Bird 13 didn't hesitate. We were being swept along in the draft of the other cars.

I scraped two cars in the turn and another going through the esses, but my jitters were gone when I hit the back straight. I passed three other drivers before the chicane.

I scrubbed through the hairpin and made it into the main straight. Kelly waved me to speed up. I did and passed another car.

My car was still heavy with fuel but handling well. I hadn't been passed yet. After a few more laps Kelly had a straggly "4" scrawled on my pit blackboard. I was racing fourth.

The next lap, on the sweeper back into the main straight, Bud Gowanus lost his Cougar in a long, tire-shredding slide. I grazed the guardrail but managed to miss him.

Bruce Adams didn't. Owens' teammate plowed into the broadsided Cougar. The red lights flashed on and I pitted.

Joe Holcombe's pit crew swarmed my car. Billy Welch shoved a cup of cold water to me.

"You're running great," Kelly told me. "Keep it up. You haven't been passed yet."

Holcombe slapped my car, the signal to go, before I could ask about Dennis.

Now I began sorting out the cars ahead of mine. Mark Owens hadn't given up his early lead, but Gus Enright's Challenger was pushing him hard. Neal Hutchinson's Mustang was ahead of me.

I concentrated on catching Hutchinson. He was cornering faster than I was, but I gained ground

39

along the straights. I was finally on his back bumper, but that's where I stayed, lap after lap.

Hutchinson wasn't obvious enough to catch McCune's eye, but whenever I tried to pass, a piece of his car was always in my way. It was frustrating but interesting too. Hutchinson was showing me tricks I would use later.

Finally I showed him one of my own. I drove as if I was going to pass under his car on the track, then topped his move by letting the rear end of my car drift. I swung wide and went over him.

Hutchinson pulled up to within an inch of my back bumper, and stayed there. My faster car was drafting his while we chased the leaders.

Owens was pulling away from Enright as we got into final laps. I was low on fuel. I suspected that my tires were getting scrubbed thin. But there was no way to shake Hutchinson.

Dennis had managed to work up and slot Green Bird 31 behind Hutchinson's Mustang.

Going through the esses, Hutchinson bunted my car. After the race, he apologized.

"I didn't mean to do it, Justin," he said. "It was just one of those things that happen in race traffic."

Green Bird was hit hard enough to swing the rear end. I overcorrected. Before I knew what was happening I was spinning out of control, end-swapping. Off the track, still spinning, I hit hay bales. My car stopped, pointing in the direction from which I'd come.

I looked across the track to find Dennis on the

grass, too, grinding away at his starter. He was pointed the right direction but going nowhere in a hurry.

My engine was still ticking over. When there was a break in traffic, I shifted into low and pulled back on the track. That's when I realized I'd tried to stop my spin by shifting down, but without using the clutch. I had one gear left, low.

Dennis passed me before I had crawled around the track to the pits, hugging the infield. When he passed, a burst of smoke from his pipes told me what his starting problem had been. Dennis had flooded the carb.

I watched the rest of the race from the pit wall with Holcombe and Kelly. Dennis drove a good catch-up race but only managed fifth place.

Mark Owens won the race going away from Gus Enright, who placed second. Chet Frazier in his Cutlass was third. Phil Spell brought his Challenger into fourth place.

Neal Hutchinson finished back in the field with a sick engine.

Only Bud Gowanus, Bruce Adams, and I failed to finish this first All-Am race.

Bud came over while we were getting ready to haul the cars back to Johnsonville. He gave Dennis a pat on the shoulder and shook hands with me. "Join the losers' club," he said. "You drove a damn fine race. Any hard feelings toward me?"

"No. You were calling it as you saw it."

Bud shrugged. "Nice of you to see it that way.

41

Sitting out this one I got a good chance to watch you fellows drive. Squirrelly you ain't."

I was more than a little surprised to find out Mother had watched the race as Mr. Johnson's guest. "We thought you'd be nervous if you knew I was here," she told me. "Dee and I yelled ourselves hoarse. I didn't have any idea car racing was this exciting."

"You must have swallowed your tongue when I spun out," I said.

Mother laughed. "I didn't see you and Dennis leave the track," she said. "Dee had to call it to my attention. Why couldn't you get back in the race? We were disappointed."

"I stripped my gears."

"Don't worry about it," Mr. Johnson said. "You drove a good race until you went out. You can wash your face at Texas International next month."

All of us there in the pits were invited by Mr. Johnson to his estate for an after-the-race barbecue. Joe Holcombe and Sam Sanford began to make their excuses.

"Damn it, y'all come," Mr. Johnson said. "I'm the chef and I'm a good one. My housekeeper and her husband, who manages my farm, will be my guests. Do you want to insult me? I'm a sensitive man about my color."

Joe laughed and winked at Sam. "You've got two more guests, Mr. Johnson."

4

Texas International Speedway is near College Station, Texas. There's a road course there, but it was decided to hold the 400-mile race on the superspeedway oval. That put Kelly to some trouble.

Car frames had to be wedged to slant right in order to compensate for constantly turning left. Two-speed gearboxes had to be installed. You shift from low to high, and Go, on a superspeedway. You take the high-banked turns at full-bore.

This would be a new type of racing for Dennis and me. Driving a twisty road course is one thing. Flying around a superspeedway oval in the 160 to 190 range is something else.

"We'll rig you two thermos jugs of ice water," Kelly told us, "that you can suck through a tube. Heat exhaustion can kill you in a long race."

We would be in our cars at least three hours. "By final laps you'll be losing your driving edge," Kelly warned us. "I've seen good drivers do some damned foolish things toward the end of long races."

Dennis and I already knew it had been a crash during final laps of the Daytona 500 that had crippled Kelly and ended his career as a driver.

Practicing for the Texas International race, Dennis and I drove the superspeedway oval at Georgetown. On that three-mile track we found out what the Green Birds could really do.

Dennis blew a right front tire doing 180 in the middle of the back straight. Despite the safety inner liner that kept the tire from going entirely flat, Dennis had a real fight for car control on his hands. He came in shaking, his face beaded with sweat. Getting out of the car, he lay on the grass, hands clasped behind his neck, and stared at the clouds sailing the sky.

I sat down beside him. "You had us worried," I said. "Feeling better?"

"Better? I guess so. I thought I'd really had it, J.J. It's creepy. You ask yourself, What am I doing in this crazy automobile? Do you want to know something? I don't know the answer."

I lost Green Bird 13 coming out of the second turn the next morning. One second I was in good shape. The next, my car was sideways, rubber screaming, and the interior filling with rubber smoke. I kept it from rolling or spinning, but just. When I finally stopped, I'd skidded more than 1,000 feet and ruined four new racing tires.

This time I came in shaking and sweating.

"Good show," Kelly said with sarcasm. "Whatever you did coming out of that turn, don't do it again. Next time it could be fatal."

Dennis had begun dating my cousin Voncil. The fact that she worked the night shift at Columbia Hospital, and on her night off wanted to sleep the clock around, presented him with courtship problems.

"I'm getting better acquainted with Mrs. Shakne than Voncil," Dennis complained. "We watch afternoon television while Voncil gets her sleep before I take her out to dinner. Have you ever watched afternoon television, J.J.?"

"Not when I could help it," I told him.

"Why can't I fall for a girl who works normal hours?" Dennis asked.

"That's a good question," I said, "but you'll have to answer it yourself."

Joe Holcombe's crew worked NASCAR and USAC races when they weren't crewing for us, but they were ready and waiting when we towed the Green Birds to College Station, Texas.

Mr. Johnson had bought a house trailer to park on the infield, a compact sixteen-footer, with the refrigerator stocked with beer, soft drinks, bread, and sandwich makings. Any of us could stretch out on the bed or couch in the trailer when we wanted to rest or nap. It was painted as green as our cars, of course.

Kelly drove the tractor pulling the car van. Dennis and I followed along in the pickup truck loaded with tires, spare parts, two spare engines, and tools. We towed the trailer.

Dennis, Kelly, and I checked into the Lone Star Motel, where the other drivers and their crew chiefs were staying. Holcombe and his crew stayed with the cars, snatching sleep in the van and trailer. You never know when some nut may tamper with an unattended race car. It has happened.

Mark Owens again nailed down pole position when he qualified. Neither Dennis nor I did well on the strange track. We ended up on the starting grid, side by side, in the next to the last row. Only Ace Allen in his Camaro and Bob Frazier's Cutlass were behind us. Ace had ignition trouble when he qualified. Gusts of wind blew Bob all over the track.

"I thought I was in a sailboat," he said when he came in. "If it's gusty tomorrow, some of us boys are going to have trouble."

It was a cloudy day when we raced, but the wind wasn't so bad as it had been late the day before when Bob had qualified his car.

"Cloud cover will keep the track surface cooler, so we shouldn't have much tire trouble," Kelly said before Dennis and I joined the starting field. "Just the same, look out for wind gusts. Stay in a low groove on the track as much as you can."

After a pace lap, we were off and running for the bottom turn. With 400 miles to go, Dennis and I agreed we'd stay out of heavy traffic until the cars strung out.

On the third lap, Bruce Adams passed his teammate, Mark Owens. Owens began drafting his Barracuda behind Adams'. Neal Hutchinson and Bob Frazier were coming on fast, two car lengths behind Adams and Owens. Gus Enright in his Challenger was trying to pass them. Phil Spell, who had made a bad start and was now trying to make up for it, had his foot heavy on the gas pedal. Spell went up to the rim of the track to pass Enright. Six cars were running too close together.

A gust of wind must have blown Spell's car down into Frazier's Cutlass.

As soon as they connected, I toed brakes, and wrenched Green Bird 13 into a slide.

Frazier's car and Spell's, locked-up, swerved into Hutchinson's Mustang. Enright drove into the mushrooming cloud of dust.

I was going into the junk-up ahead sideways. That was no good. I jerked my Green Bird straight, hung onto the steering wheel, and prayed.

Dust blinded me. Car pieces and parts pelted Green Bird 13. I was out of the mess as suddenly as I'd driven into it, my car more or less intact. My windshield was cracked and there was a dent in the hood, but that was all the damage I could see.

Slowing down, I looked back. Phil Spell's wrecked car was upside down on the infield. The other cars were in a tangle on the track. The drivers were out of their cars and wandering around the mess dazedly.

Phil was still in his car.

The ambulance and fire truck were coming across the infield. Dennis had parked and was running toward Phil's car. I swung off the track, parked, wriggled out of my car, and ran to meet Dennis.

Phil's Challenger was a mess! He was either unconscious or dead, hanging upside down from his seat belt and shoulder harness.

Fuel fumes rose like heat waves from the car.

"We've got to get him out," Dennis said, on his knees and reaching inside the car. "Help me, J.J."

"I'm trying to." I was on my knees, too, trying to hit Phil's seat belt buckle. "Where is the damned thing?"

Dennis had loosened Phil's shoulder harness. I finally hit the seat belt release. Phil dropped out of his bucket seat.

The car exploded before we could grab his arms. The blast knocked Dennis and me back about ten feet, but neither of us was burned.

The fire truck had arrived. Firemen in fireproof suits with face shields waded into the flames and pulled Phil out.

The attendants swung off the rear step of the ambulance and reached Phil.

One shook his head. "Too damned bad," he said to Dennis and me. He pointed to the seared flesh that had once been a face. "Flames got him."

Dennis jerked off his helmet, bent his head, and swore softly. I crossed myself and said a prayer. The attendants lifted Phil onto a stretcher and covered his face and body with a blanket.

Without speaking to each other, Dennis and I went back to our cars and drove around to the pits. They already had the word that Phil was dead.

"You guys tried," Kelly said in a grim voice. "Damn it!" He smacked his fist into the palm of his other hand. "We had drinks together just last night."

Dennis and I, with the race stopped until the track could be cleared, headed for the trailer. We sat on the couch, staring into space.

Dennis spoke first. "We tried, Kelly says!"

"I know. If I'd been quicker with that seat belt release, we might have got him out."

"Racing!" Dennis was bitter. "Voncil wants me to give it up. I wish I could."

"We're both hooked," I told him.

Kelly stuck his head in the door. "We'll be racing in ten minutes, fellows."

We did another pace lap, got the green flag, and were off.

The wrecks bulldozed off the back straight and Phil's still-smouldering car should have slowed us down. Just the opposite was true. Everyone still racing kept his foot on the floor.

The raw power of Kelly's Green Birds, now we could drive them flat-out, was soon apparent. Dennis and I had the fastest machinery still racing.

We plunged around the oval, blowing off one car after another, pushing our tach needles into the red danger zone when we had to.

During pit stops, Joe Holcombe and his crew swarmed our cars. Kelly didn't tell us to slow down. "Break your cars if you have to, but try to win this one," he said.

On final laps, we had only Mark Owens to catch and pass. We were side by side on his rear bumper when we got the white flag, signaling the last lap. We

49

bracketed Owens down the main straight. All three of us crowded through the bottom turn.

We got past Owens on the back straight. Dennis and I came across the start-finish less than a second apart. It wasn't until we had done our extra lap and came into the pits that I knew I'd won the photo-finish race.

Mark Owens finished third. Bud Gowanus steered his Mercury Cougar into fourth place.

With 19 points we were leading the All-Am series. Mark Owens' Plymouth team had 16 points. The Fords had 5.

Owens was the individual driver with the most points, 16. I had 10. Dennis had 9, and Enright 8. Dennis and I were no longer rookies.

The winning purse was $10,000. Dennis earned $5,000 by placing second. Mr. Johnson insisted we take our 25 percent cut, but the rest of the money he sent along to Mrs. Spell in Brookline, Massachusetts. She had three children to raise.

All the other drivers chipped in money to send to Mrs. Spell. Mark Owens had come to this race in style, flown here in his personal plane, a Lear jet. Phil's body was flown home by Mark.

For the race at Watkins Glen, Dodge would track a new Challenger and contracted with a Canadian driver, Jo Davidson, to race it. Jo was better known on the European Grand Prix circuit than he was in his own country and the United States.

We would race 300 miles at Watkins Glen. Mark

Owens had scored on this road track twice before and was favored to win.

"Every time sports writers do that to me," Mark told Dennis and me, "it's like a double whammy. I get out there and go no place."

Watkins Glen, a sleepy resort town at the south end of Seneca Lake in upper New York State, is called the "Cradle of American Road Racing." Every driver wants the prestige of a win at The Glen.

It's a tough course. From the start-finish you have a long, wide straight, but at the end of it is a 90-degree left turn into a short straight, which takes you into what they call The Fast Bend. From there you race to The Chute.

The Chute is trouble because it's a 180-degree hairpin that sends you back from where you've come. If you come through that one intact, you're into a series of hairy right and left swings before you go into the sweeper that takes you back into the main straight to the start-finish.

We raced at The Glen the last Sunday in April. Dennis and I practiced on the track a week before the race and thought we had it down pat. After our win at Texas International we were a cocky pair. The shock of Phil's sudden death had worn off. We drove at the track up there as if there wasn't a tomorrow. Kelly warned us about overconfidence.

"You were lucky back in Texas," he said, "but every driver will be out there to see you don't get that lucky again."

When the green flag dropped at The Glen that

warm Sunday afternoon, we soon found out what Kelly had tried to tell us. Jo Davidson, a chunky little man with blond hair, challenged Mark Owens for the lead early in the race. Dennis and I had been slow getting away. We were way back in the field.

We stayed back there, too, for the first 100 miles. We couldn't pass anybody. One driver after another blocked our attempts to pass. Finally, Bob Frazier's Cutlass kept getting in our way.

Frazier knew The Glen almost as well as Owens did. Where it was impossible for us to pass, say through The Chute, he'd grin and wave us to come on. Where we could pass, he managed to stay in our way. It went like that, lap after lap, until Dennis and I were boiling.

Both of us, driving mad, had the same crazy idea —pass him through The Chute. So the next time Frazier waved us on going into The Chute, we came after him like Gangbusters. Three cars scrubbing through The Chute together is disaster, and Frazier knew it, so he braked and let us have at it.

There's a shunt there, an alley by which you can leave the track if you see you're not going to make it. Dennis and I ignored it. But we were into The Chute much too fast.

The left side of his car slammed into the right side of mine. Dennis spun right, I spun left, and we were on the grass, still swapping ends. Then we slammed together, this time the left side of my car tearing up the right side of his.

There was no question of getting back into the

race. Our cars were too torn up.

Frazier came around again and gave us a cheerful wave. The rest of the drivers were amused, too, when they found us sitting in our cars, side by side, off the track.

Dennis unbuckled his helmet and dropped it in his lap. "At least we picked a good spot from which to watch this race, J.J.," he said.

"Yeah, and we sure showed Bob Frazier, didn't we?"

Dennis nodded. "That we did. Kelly isn't going to like the way we've torn up his cars, you know."

"I don't expect he will," I said. "Your father, either. We blew this one, all right."

Just then Kelly and Mr. Johnson came rattling up in our pickup truck from an access road.

"You boys all right?" Mr. Johnson asked.

"Just fine," Dennis said. "Just fine."

Kelly walked around the cars, inspecting the damage with a sour expression on his face, kicking at the tires.

Dennis and I sat in our cars, arms crossed on our chests, watching the race.

Now Kelly studied the maze of skid marks we'd left. Finally he spoke to Dennis and me.

"Who did you two speed tramps try to pass here?" he asked.

"Frazier." It was Dennis who spoke.

"Well, did you pass him?"

"Oh, yes, we sure enough did," I told Kelly. "Both of us passed him. We just couldn't get by each other."

"Damned fool race drivers!" Kelly muttered. "Jell-O for brains."

Mark Owens blew his engine on the final lap and Jo Davidson won the race. Neal Hutchinson was second, Bob Frazier, third, and Bruce Adams nosed his Plymouth Barracuda into fourth place.

Adams' driving gave Plymouth the team lead with 20 points to our 19. The Fords now had 13 points, and so did the Dodges. The Cutlass team had to settle for 6.

Despite going DNF, Mark Owens with his 16 points still led the individual standings.

We had two Green Birds to rebuild before the May race at Road Atlanta. That road course is near Gainesville, Georgia, and it's another tough one to drive.

After our miserable showing at The Glen, Dennis and I would have to sharpen up for the 350-mile race at Road Atlanta. If we didn't, Mr. Johnson was going to be in trouble with Pontiac.

5

After we came back from the fiasco at The Glen, there was a lot of sheet metal work to be done before tracking the Green Birds at Road Atlanta. Perfectionist Kelly kept Dennis and me hammering, sanding, and painting until we were dizzy. Kelly took grim satisfaction in watching us repair the damage we'd done to the cars.

I spent most of my between-races time at the Johnson estate, where Mr. and Mrs. Keller began to regard me as family. Dee needed help with her math homework and I gave it to her when I wasn't too tired. She taught me how to ride a horse. I only fell off twice.

"Stick to racing cars, J.J.," Dee advised me. "A cowboy you're not."

I didn't see much of either Mr. Johnson or Dennis. Both of them were commuting to Columbia on a nightly basis. Mr. Johnson, so he said, was trying to close a real estate deal and open a Green Front store in Columbia. Dennis, of course, was dating Voncil.

I borrowed a car and had two Sunday dinners with Mother. If she missed me being around all the time when I wasn't working, she didn't say so. She seemed happier, as a matter of fact, than I'd seen her in a long while.

Mr. Johnson was thoughtful enough to introduce Dennis and me to his tax accountant. He advised us each to open a tax account with one of the Johnsonville banks so any money we might make racing wouldn't get us into year-end trouble with the Internal Revenue Service. This we did.

When you're professional, you live from race to race. I had no plans for myself when the All-Am series wound up. I didn't intend to work offshore, however. Six on and six off would be deadly boring after the excitement of racing. The sport gets into your blood.

When the cars were back in shape I worked with Kelly, installing turbo superchargers.

"All of the cars will get quicker as the series goes on," Kelly told me. "We've got to keep the acceleration and speed edge we have."

"I'll take your word for it," I said, "but the Green Birds are fast enough for me right now."

While we reworked the engines, Kelly got to know me better. "Mark Owens has a degree from M.I.T. in mechanical engineering," Kelly said one evening when we'd finished work. "You're handy with tools and have a greasy thumb, J.J. You ought to get an engineering education one day."

"I'll think about it," I promised.

"You do that, and think hard," Kelly went on to say. "Racing is a mean and cruel sport, and you'd

56

better believe that. Drivers always think accidents happen to the other guy, and never to them, but you can catch it as fast as Phil Spell did. Or you can get crippled up like me."

"You seem to be doing all right, Kelly."

"Oh, sure, using a damned cane, and with a leg that hurts most of the time. I'm one of the lucky ones. Go back ten years sometime, J.J., and see how many top drivers are still above the ground. You'll find mighty damned few. Racing is all I've ever known since I got off the farm. You can do better for yourself."

"Maybe, Kelly, but I like racing and want to find out how good I am at it. After that, who knows? What about Mark Owens? He has all the money he'll ever need and a university degree. Why is he out there on the track?"

"Because he can't help himself," Kelly said. "For all his easygoing ways, Mark has a competitive edge you wouldn't believe. He *has* to race. Mark is building a pair of Formula 1 cars right now to race the European Grand Prix circuit next season. He won't quit until he kills himself, or has the stature of men like Stirling Moss or Jim Clarke."

"You seem to know a lot about Mark Owens. How come?"

"I worked for him once and probably will again. When I was down, out, and broke, after my accident, it was Mark who gave me a job. Most of what I know about preparing cars to race I learned from Mark."

"How old is Mark? He looks about twenty four or

five, but he's been around a long time."

"Mark's thirty-four," Kelly told me. "His age doesn't show. He should be a world champion before he's forty. If he's smart, that's when Mark will hang up his helmet and racing gear."

"I like the guy," I said.

"Almost everyone does, off the track," Kelly told me. "But he's one tough cookie steering a racing car. I guess you've found that out, though."

The main straight of Road Atlanta ends in a short right turn, then you're driving along a "wavy" straight, and a long one. From there you're into an open hairpin, or U-turn. I spent a lot of practice time driving *that* corner, after the fiasco back at The Glen.

You can really push your car along the straight after the U-turn. There isn't enough bend in it to cause car control trouble.

Next there's a right turn, a short straight, and another right, after that a short dash to the start-finish line.

Road Atlanta is a hilly course. This makes suspension a problem. If it isn't stiff enough, your car goes light coming over the top of a hill, heavy on the down slopes.

Dennis and I arrived a week before the race to practice and learn the track. With the exception of Mark Owens, all the other drivers were early arrivals too.

Before the race at Texas International, and the one at The Glen, Dennis and I had behaved ourselves, staying out of bars and away from liquid refreshments served by automobile and accessory manufacturers to all comers. We were no longer rookies, however, and now found we had been accepted into the clannish society of professional race drivers.

"Come along down to the Royal Tire suite," Ace Allen would say. "They've got some real nifty hostesses and the drinks aren't watered."

Along with Ace we'd go. Some evenings we had a hard time finding our room at the Atlanta Motor Hotel. But we would commute out to the track at Gainesville early, if not too bright, the next morning. Both of us had a rental car. Neither of us could stand the other's driving.

I collected one speeding ticket and Dennis got two.

Thursday was a heavy night for us. We played poker with Bob and Chet Frazier, Jo Davidson, Bruce Adams, and Walt Fischer. It was four o'clock before Walt had all the chips. Kelly wanted us at the track at eight. We arrived at nine, red-eyed and more than slightly hung over.

Kelly had hauled an oxygen tank into the pits and ordered us to take deep-breathing exercises before he unloaded.

"Where did you bums get the idea that every night is New Year's Eve?" Kelly asked when we were partially revived. "These other good-buddy drivers have been around tracks long enough to celebrate all night and drive the next day, but you two are cream puffs. You're also stupid. Qualifying trials are tomorrow. Cut that party in Enright's room, dry up, and get your sleep."

"We've got your message, Kelly," I told him. "No party tonight and plenty of sleep."

"There's more," Kelly said. "You guys have been racing each other in those U-Wreck-Em cars, which ain't safe and also gives race drivers a bad name. Cut that out."

"Yes, sir," Dennis said. "Now how did he find out about that?" Dennis asked when Kelly started to walk away.

Kelly heard him and came back. "You're my drivers," he said, stabbing a finger at us. "It's my business to know even when and if you go to the bathroom. So now shape up, do you hear?"

Walking away again, Kelly asked over his shoulder, "How much did you lose last night? And don't either of you know better than trying to fill an inside straight?"

"It was Dennis who lost that hand," I called after Kelly, but he wasn't listening.

Gus Enright in his Challenger was the fastest qualifier, with Neal Hutchinson grabbing the outside slot in the front row. Mark Owens hadn't arrived until Friday, the day before qualifying trials. He had never driven Road Atlanta before, but in his Barracuda, Mark was third fastest qualifier.

Like our cars, both of his were now supercharged. Mark had also added wings over their back ends for better rear-wheel traction.

60

I fouled a sparkplug qualifying Green 13 and wound up at the tail end of the pack. Jo Davidson had mechanical problems with his Challenger, too, and would share idiot's row with me.

Not long after the race had started, Dennis fulfilled Kelly's prophecy. From up in the field he did some fancy charging and took an early lead, ignoring Kelly's slow-down signals. All of us knew he was going too fast and driving over his head, so we laid back to let him have at it.

Sure enough, he blew his engine and had to coast into the pits.

Ace Allen in his Camaro took the lead.

Walt Fischer's Monte Carlo was a car length behind him. Mark Owens was in third place. The wing helped him speed through the corners.

Jo Davidson, who had fought his way through traffic with me, was running fourth with my Green Bird right behind him. So I was running fifth when I made my first pit stop. But I was no sooner back on the track than Bruce Adams whizzed past me, dropping me back to sixth place.

Now Bob Frazier blew his engine. On the next lap, the engine in Neal Hutchinson's Mustang lunched, and he was DNF. That left only nine cars still running.

It was stifling hot in the car and I began fighting drowsiness, probably because of the sleep I'd missed recently. Going through the turn into the main straight, Davidson hit an oil slick and spun out. Adams had to swerve down to the infield to miss him.

I saw driving room above Davidson's spinning car and took it, missing his front end by an inch. *That* woke me up!

In fourth place, my engine began to overheat. I slipped in behind Owens to draft a few laps. This took strain off my engine, and the cushion of air my car was pushing gave Owens a boost.

Neither Davidson nor Adams could catch us. Owens shook me loose and passed Fischer. My engine was sweet again so I began moving up.

Coming into the U-turn, when brake lights ahead of me winked, I kept my foot off the pedal. I went in deeper than I ever had in practice and had to stand on the brakes. I slid farther drifting than I had before, managed to come out fast, but with my car whipping all over the track. It was touch and go, but I finally had full control.

I was also leading. I could pick and choose any driving line I preferred. It was time to let everything hang out and pray the car would hold together long enough for me to finish.

I was going to have to pit for fuel, oil, and outside tires, but Allen, Owens, and Fischer had a pit stop coming up too. I signaled Kelly I was coming in after the next lap. My fuel tank was nearly empty.

When I did come in, I was traveling too fast, and my spotter, Jerry Bryan, had to climb the pit wall like a monkey to stay out of my way. I had overshot and the rule book said I would have to make another lap.

I didn't think I could do it without running out of

fuel, but I did. I had no sooner stopped than the engine died.

Joe Holcombe and his crew got me out in record time. All I had to do now was keep my foot on the floor and aim the car. That's exactly what I did, and there's no better feeling in car racing than to have that steward at the start-finish wave the checkered flag in your face and then point it at you.

I got a royal welcome from Kelly, Mr. Johnson, Dennis, the pit crew, and Dee. She put her arms around my neck and kissed me on the cheek, smudging her nose with track dirt.

Mark Owens strolled over, swinging his helmet, without a hair out of place. He looked more rested and relaxed than he had before the race started.

"Justin, how in the devil did you get by all three of us like that?" Mark asked. "I've never seen anything like it. You'll have to give me a driving lesson one day."

"Mark, I couldn't do it again," I said. "It was purely luck I didn't lose my car and wreck."

"Rub some of your luck on me, will you?" Mark grinned. "I was sure I could win this one and not have to settle for second place. You can drive with the best, J.J."

I'd won another $2500, my share of the $10,000 first money. Our Green Birds were leading the series again with 29 points. Mark Owens' Plymouth team now had 28. The Ford, and Dodges had 14 points apiece, the Chevrolets 12, and the Oldsmobiles 7.

Mark Owens was still the driver with the most points. He had garnered 24. I had 20 points now.

Dennis was philosophical about his blown engine and sitting out most of the race. "Kelly didn't give me as much hell as I thought he would," Dennis told me. "He told me it was practice for when I'm an M.D. and lose a patient."

Dennis and I were in the pickup truck, towing back to Johnsonville after the race. We didn't plan on stopping anywhere until we had the Green Birds back in the shop. Joe Holcombe was spelling Kelly at the wheel of the tractor pulling our car van.

It was midnight Sunday when we pulled into a truck stop for coffee.

Dennis was moody and hadn't said anything for the past two hours. I knew something was eating away at him but didn't want to probe.

While we were having coffee, Kelly sensed Dennis' mood and said, "Still worried about blowing your engine?"

"No, it isn't that," Dennis said. He had finished his coffee and waved away the waitress when she wanted to give him a refill. "The summer term at Tulane starts in June. I want to get back on the campus. Premed is tough. The longer I lay out, the harder it will be to study again."

"You're fed up with racing." Kelly stated it as a fact.

Dennis nodded. "I'm scared on the track, too, after Phil Spell's accident. I have nightmares about that,

64

only it's me in the car instead of Phil."

"It's time for you to pack in racing, Dennis," Kelly said.

Joe nodded agreement. "You're a good driver, Dennis, but you have too much imagination. For race driving, that is. You'll be a damned fine M.D. We need good doctors more than we need race drivers."

"Who will drive Green Bird 31?" Dennis asked Kelly. "I don't want to let either the team or my father down."

"I know a good West Coast driver who's been pestering me for a ride in a solid, well-prepared car. Don't worry about your replacement. That's my problem. Go back to school and forget racing."

Dennis heaved a sigh of relief. "Well, that's settled, then."

"Who do you have in mind?" Joe asked Kelly.

"Shaw Lockhart. The kid's good and deserves a break. Right now he's instructing at a race driving school out in California."

"Is that Billy Lockhart's son?" Joe asked. "The Lockhart that was killed up on the salt flats trying to set a new land speed record?"

"Right," Kelly said. "I raced with Billy more than once on the NASCAR circuit. Crazy Billy we used to call him. That guy never knew when he was going fast enough."

"If there's much of his father in him," Joe said, "Shaw should be the right driver to do the job for you."

"I'll bring him on and see how it goes at Road

65

America and Mid-Ohio next month," Kelly said. "By the way, I'm going to copy Mark Owens and try wings on our cars. What do you think, Joe?"

"I think it's a good idea," Joe said. "If they don't help, we can always tear them off. They improved the handling of Mark's cars this race."

Before we were towing again, Kelly took me aside. "You'll be driving with Shaw and living with him, J.J.," he told me. "The kid's about your age, but he's had a tough time coming up. His mother died shortly after his father was killed."

"Are you trying to tell me Shaw will be hard to get along with?" I asked.

"Put it this way," Kelly said. "You may find that Shaw isn't easy to get along with, on or off the track. He deserves a break like this, but he ain't going to get it unless we give it to him."

"I'll get along with Shaw," I promised. "I've .worked and lived with some pretty rough characters."

6

May 30 is Mother's birthday. I make it a point to bring her flowers on that date and take her out to dinner. With a new engine to install in Green Bird 31, between races I stayed at the Johnson estate, but May 29 I phoned Mother about having dinner with me the next evening.

We had a strange conversation. "I surely do appreciate you remembering my birthday, J.J.," she said, "but I don't know if I can make it tomorrow night."

I'd already made reservations at The Embers in Monroe, for three because I wanted Dee to join us, so I was taken aback. "Do you have to work?" I asked.

"No, it isn't that," my mother said.

"Well, what is the problem?" I asked. "We always have dinner out on your birthday. I've ordered a cake, and have tickets to a show at the Civic Center."

"Where are you now?" she asked.

"At the shop. We're working on a car."

"Give me the number, J.J. I'll call you back in a few minutes."

Kelly gave me a narrow look when I came back to work on the new engine. "Is anything wrong?" he asked. "You look as if you'd lost your last friend."

"Nothing like that," I said. "I'm puzzled, is all. Mother is acting strangely."

Kelly grinned. "Mothers are people too."

"I guess so," I said. "Their kids have a way of forgetting that."

I was called to the phone.

"We have a date for tomorrow night," Mother said. "What time shall I be ready?"

"Six o'clock? I'm bringing Dee with me. I hope that's all right."

"Oh, yes," Mother told me. "I want to get acquainted with her."

Despite my helping with her homework, Dee had drawn a D on a math quiz Miss Hardscrabble, as she called her teacher, had given the class. "That old woman is driving me out of my tree," she told me while we were driving from Johnsonville to Columbia. "She treats me as if I was retarded or something. So long as I can add two and two to get four, what more do I need to know?"

"When you add two and two," I told her, "you're liable to come up with six or seven. You've got a brain. I don't know why math ties it up in knots."

"You sound just like Dennis and Daddy," she said, and pouted the rest of the way to Columbia.

I had presented Mother with a dozen red roses before I saw another dozen already in a vase. "Where did those come from?" I asked.

Mother blushed. "You ask too many questions," she said.

Mother and Dee hit it off fine. During dinner Dee was talking a mile a minute. Mother kept up with her. I ate my steak and wondered if they would ever run down.

The touring company at the Civic did well, I thought, with a Broadway comedy, *Barefoot in the Park*. Dee was taking home ec, so between acts she and Mother swapped recipes.

"I love your mother," Dee told me while we were driving back to Johnsonville.

"That makes two of us," I said.

"You're very lucky, J.J."

"I think so, too, Dee."

Shaw Lockhart drove straight through from Los Angeles to Johnsonville in a battered old Impala with a cracked windshield. Mr. Johnson had invited Shaw to stay at his home while he was in Johnsonville between races. Instead, Shaw checked into an inexpensive motel when he arrived.

I met him when he reported to Kelly at the shop. He was named for the great race driver Wilbur Shaw. He stood a scant five-nine and was thin, so thin, in fact, I wondered if he had been eating regularly.

Shaw's face tapered to a stubborn mouth and a strong chin. High cheekbones flanked a long, thin nose, and his eyes were a milky blue. Shaggy brown hair dripped over his collar.

At first I thought he was shy, but I soon learned I was wrong. Shaw was simply withdrawn and hid his feelings with a poker face.

69

He gave me a limp handshake when Kelly introduced us. "I read about your last race," he said.

"I was pretty lucky, I guess."

"I think a driver makes his own luck," Shaw said. "Savvy and a strong car win races."

"Maybe so. Glad to have you with us, Shaw."

"When can I start driving?" he asked Kelly.

"Ain't but a little to do on the new engine in your car," Kelly said. "How about this afternoon? We have permission to use the superspeedway over at Georgetown."

"Suits me," Shaw said. "The sooner the better. I don't want to get rusty."

That afternoon Shaw took Green Bird 31 out on the track first. We expected him to idle around for a dozen laps, getting acquainted with the car, but when he had completed one warm-up lap Shaw put his foot into the mill.

Kelly and I watched him go.

"That kid is a fast learner," Kelly remarked. "One lap and he's learned the track."

It was true. On an established driving line Shaw was cutting laps in the 180 to 185 mph range. He made it look easy. He sat straight and handled the car with stiff arms.

Shaw turned twenty laps before he came in.

"How does it feel?" I asked while he was wriggling out of the car.

Shaw dusted his hands and pulled off his driving gloves. "Okay. She understeers a bit too much to suit me," he told Kelly.

70

I took out Green Bird 13, determined to prove I was as good behind the wheel as Shaw. If I have a main fault, always trying to prove something is it.

So what happens? I was building speed down the back straight when a rabbit got his fill of clover and came hopping across the track. With the needle nudging 183, steering to miss a rabbit is something you don't do, but I did.

The rear end broke loose and the telltale rumble coming up the steering post told me the front end was going too.

"Damn!" I was into a screaming slide with rubber smoke filling the car.

I thought I was going to smash into the guardrail on the banked turn coming up, but the skid killed just enough speed for me to feather the throttle and grab the car straight before I was into the turn.

Bobbling like that, with Shaw watching, made me mad at myself. I cut another fast lap before I came into the pits.

Shaw watched me get out of the car, sitting on the pit wall with an expressionless face.

"What was that all about?" Kelly asked in a mild voice. "You must like to drive that back straight side-wise."

His comment didn't soothe my temper. "Would you believe a rabbit was on the track?" I snapped.

Kelly shook his head. "No."

"To hell with you then," I said and stalked away, swinging my helmet.

When I looked back, Shaw had walked over to my

car to kick the right front tire. With a pop the tire blew out.

"You know better than not to come in right away after scrubbing tires like you did," Kelly called after me.

"Yeah, I know better," I said, calming down. "Sorry about that."

Shaw had fired up Green Bird 31 and was out cutting more flawless laps.

Road America is a four-mile circuit, 65 miles from Milwaukee and two miles east of Elkhart Lake, a resort town. We would race 400 miles here.

It's an uphill, downhill track winding through a park with shaded hillsides. Spectators have it good at Road America.

It's a different matter for race drivers. You drive a long straight from the start-finish, then find yourself navigating a 90-degree turn. Another 90-degree right turn comes up almost immediately.

The straight after that turn dips under a bridge. This isn't good. The bridge shadow is bothersome and careless spectators drop debris on the track. During a Road America race, one driver got a beer can through his windshield that could have torn his head off.

You turn 90 degrees again at the end of that straight, pass under a second bridge, make another 90-degree left turn, swing through a left-right bend, and you're into a 180-degree open hairpin. This one is a real car-breaker unless you drift through it just right.

After that one there's a sweeper, a short straight, two 90-degree turns, and you're back into the main straight to cross the start-finish line.

Both the Chevrolets and the Fords had wings mounted, as did our Green Birds, and all the cars sported superchargers. More speed was going to be the name of this game. Drivers were averaging 110 mph around the course, no sweat.

I was quicker than Shaw during practice because most of his racing experience had been on oval tracks. But coming up to the race he kept improving. I was going to have a time of it beating my own teammate.

Shaw kept to himself. We had separate rooms at the Elkhart Motel and didn't eat together.

I missed the easy companionship of Dennis. The only communication between Shaw and me was in the pits or the garage and concerning the cars. Shaw was a genuine loner.

The All-Am race at Road America was a classic. Kelly planned for me to set the pace early in the race. Shaw was to hang back for the first 200 miles. He figured that way at least one of our cars would be in contention at the finish.

"Get up front and stay there," Kelly had told me. "Let other drivers chase you."

It was good advice, but too many other drivers had

73

the same idea. It was impossible to lead this race for even a single lap. Ace Allen, Walt Fischer, Neal Hutchinson, Bud Gowanus, Mark Owens, and Bruce Adams stayed right with me. Seven of us were bunched together.

Seconds behind us, Shaw, the Fraziers, Gus Enright, and Jo Davidson came along. That was a five-car traffic jam.

All of us drove as if this were the end of the race, not the beginning. I had visions of all twelve cars rolling up in a massive ball of junk if anyone got out of shape.

At the speeds we were driving it had to happen sooner or later. Adams passed me coming through the hairpin to take the lead I'd just taken away from Owens. I saw his rear end begin to swing, and managed to swerve around Adams, but Owens wasn't as lucky. Adams' Plymouth got broadside and Owens rammed into him. That was the end of the race for the Plymouth team.

By some miracle the rest of the drivers didn't hit the wrecked cars. With yellow caution lights on until the track was cleared, Shaw, the Fraziers, Enright, and Davidson edged up on Allen, Fischer, Hutchinson, Gowanus, and me. When the race went on the green, ten cars were running inches apart.

It took fancy driving to string out through the turns and bunch up again down the straights, and all of us were getting some metal laid on.

Kelly signaled Shaw and me to drop back. I slowed down but Shaw missed the signal or ignored it. Enright's engine blew, spinning his car. Brake lights twinkled, and cars were all over the track trying to miss Enright's Challenger. I detoured over the infield markers.

Shaw never took his foot off the gas pedal. Scraping through the gaggle of cars, he had the lead before caution lights came on.

The field began stringing out. I worked my way up into sixth place. Shaw was still leading when he got into the hairpin too fast, skidding into Allen's car. Both of them went DNF at that point.

Fischer's Monte Carlo led now. I got past Gowanus into third place behind Hutchinson's Mustang. I made my first pit stop. All the other drivers pitted too.

Shaw was sitting on the wall, kicking his feet. He had stripped off his driving suit and was wearing a pair of baggy slacks and a shirt. He didn't raise a hand to me when I came in.

The best-trained pit crew can have an off day. I managed to kill the engine and had a hard time getting it fired up again. That was only the beginning.

My car fell off the jacks when Pablo and Olaf had pulled the outside wheels. Billy snapped the retaining chain on the oil cap. It fell into the blistering hot engine.

While Billy was fishing for the cap with a wire coat hanger, Sam spilled a can of fuel. Joe's quick work with a fire extinguisher saved Green Bird 13 from exploding.

By this time I was swearing and so was Kelly. Shaw

watched all this, still kicking his feet, with no expression on his thin face.

When Joe finally thumped my trunk with his fist, I'd been in the pits more than five minutes. I spurted out on the track, dead-last in the race with the nearest car half a lap ahead of me. I didn't have a chance to improve my position.

Fischer won the race, Hutchinson finished second, Gowanus came in third, and Davidson copped fourth. Only two other cars finished. Six cars were the only ones running when the checkered flag dropped.

Joe had a long face. "We sure booted it this time and lost you the race, J.J.," he said. "I'm sorry as hell."

"Forget it, Joe," I told him. "This just wasn't our day. Maybe we've used up all our bad luck."

I was down and feeling grim, however, when we were towing back to Johnsonville. Shaw was in the pickup sharing the driving chore. When he wasn't at the wheel Shaw watched the scenery and kept his mouth shut.

"As the fellow said," I remarked, "things could be worse and next week, sure enough, they got worse."

"Yeah," Shaw said.

"You don't talk much," I told him.

"Yeah," Shaw said again.

"Too bad you cracked up. You were driving a good race."

"Yeah."

76

Bad luck dogged me when we raced the Mid-Ohio Sports Car circuit. Bob and Chet Frazier took their Cutlasses up front after the first few laps, to lead the car parade all the way. They were hot and nobody could get by them.

Mark Owens blew his engine trying to catch the Fraziers. I couldn't do anything right. Early in the race I wiped out second and third gears in my car trying to get through a hairy turn they call The Keyhole. Able to use only first and fourth slowed me considerably. Every other car in the race lapped me.

Rain squalls slowed the race, but Shaw was expert going in the wet. He finished right behind the Fraziers, but had chopped Ace Allen coming into the main straight on the final lap.

Ace jumped the head steward as soon as he was out of his car. "Aren't you going to disqualify that crazy S.O.B.?" he asked. "He cut me so short I had to stand on my brakes."

The steward watching that corner had been looking elsewhere.

Kelly got into the hassle. He and Ace nearly came to blows. Shaw stood apart and watched.

When the stewards finally refused to disqualify Shaw, Ace was still steaming. He walked over to Shaw, said something to him, and launched a wild swing at his jaw. Shaw snapped his head back, avoiding Ace's fist, then he grabbed Ace's other arm, put a hip into him, and threw Ace on his back.

Shaw dusted his hands and walked away.

I gave Ace a hand to his feet and slapped his back to help him get his wind. All the anger was out of him. "Boy, did I ask for that," Ace said in a wry voice. "What gives with that guy? A cigar-store Indian has a better personality."

"If I ever find out," I told Ace, "I'll let you know. Shaw is hard to figure."

Kelly got on Shaw for cutting Ace off. "You ain't going to make friends driving like that," he said. "Count yourself lucky that corner steward was watching some bird in a miniskirt instead of the track."

"Yeah," Shaw said. "I had to do it to finish third."

We were still leading with 35 points, but the Fords had 30, the Chevrolets 23, the Oldsmobiles 27, and the Dodges 20. Mark Owens' Plymouths had 29 points. Obviously no team was going to run away with this series of races.

Owens was the leading individual driver with 24 points, and I was next with 22. Fischer, Hutchinson, and Chet Frazier each had 18 points. Bob Frazier and Davidson had 16 points. Allen and Gowanus had 13, Enright 11, Adams 7, and Lockhart 6.

With four races during July and August, any of us could win $150,000.

We would race 350 miles at Dallas International and 250 miles at Donnybrooke during July. In August we would go to California for the 250-mile Laguna Seca race, and 500 miles at either Riverside or Ontario.

7

When we got back to Johnsonville, Dennis was on cloud nine because the Shaknes had just announced his engagement to Voncil. They would be married next September and rent an apartment near Tulane. Voncil had a job lined up down there at Charity Hospital.

"Wrecking your Triumph was the best thing that ever happened to me," Dennis told me. "I'd like you to be best man at our wedding."

"Okay. I'll try not to lose the ring. And before I forget it, congratulations. Voncil has always been my favorite cousin. If she cooks like her mother, you're going to be a fat doctor."

Dennis laughed. "I'll take that chance. When are you going to find yourself a girl?"

"That's a good question, Dennis, but I don't know the answer. The cute little birds who hang around the pits, trying to pick up race drivers, just don't turn me on. Between races I have darn little time to go hunting, if I knew where to hunt."

Dee joined us in the living room. "Miss Hardscrabble rides again, J.J.," she said. "I have a math quiz tomorrow. Do you suppose you can help me review?"

"In a minute," I told her.

"What do you make of Shaw Lockhart?" Dennis asked me. "Talking to him is like speaking to a post. I can't figure the guy."

"Neither can I, but he can drive, there's no mistake about that after Mid-Ohio. Shaw can also take care of himself. You should have seen him toss Ace Allen when they had a run-in after the race."

Dennis and Mr. Johnson had missed the last two races. Dennis was busy dating Voncil, and Mr. Johnson had urgent business appointments.

"I heard about that," Dennis said. "Myself, I wouldn't want to mix it with a big guy like Ace. Shaw must have some tiger in him."

"Are you fellows going to talk all night?" Dee wanted to know.

"Coming," I told her.

There's always more to do between races than you think can be done. Kelly decided we could lighten the Green Birds by pulling the body shells and dipping them in acid. Of course, after the acid bath had eaten off layers of metal, we had to repaint the cars. Then they had to be waxed and polished.

We scattered the engine of Green Bird 13 for a complete overhaul. All parts were magnafluxed for any signs of excessive wear. We found a hairline crack in the crankshaft and replaced it.

We had raced on Pirelli rubber so far. Now the

Firestone people wanted their tires on the cars. They made Mr. Johnson a money offer he couldn't refuse. That meant three days of tire-testing at Georgetown, with a Firestone engineer in attendance, before Kelly was satisfied with the new rubber.

I worked with Kelly, getting the cars ready for Dallas International, but Shaw didn't lift a wrench. He let it be known he was a race driver, and not a mechanic. He stayed in the shop so he would know what was going on, but read a book most of the time.

A week before time to leave for the race, Shaw came into the shop one morning with a telegram he showed Kelly.

"Since she was my mother I'll have to go to the funeral," I overheard him tell Kelly. "I'll drive straight through to the coast and back in time for the race."

Shaw left for his motel to pack. Kelly went over to the plant to see Mr. Johnson. When he came back in a few minutes, he said, "J.J., come here a minute."

Kelly handed me money. "Shaw's flying out there and back. Mr. Johnson has made a reservation on Delta's eleven forty flight."

"What if he doesn't want to fly?"

"That's your problem," Kelly told me. "Twist his arm a little. We want him back here in shape to race."

I was using the Johnson Mercedes that day and caught Shaw at his motel, ready to toss his suitcase into the trunk of the Impala. Getting out of the Mercedes, I took the case away from him. "Orders from

Mr. Johnson," I told him. "You're flying to Los Angeles and back."

"I don't have the fare."

"That's taken care of." I put his suitcase on the back seat of the Mercedes. "Hop in. We just have time to make your flight."

Shaw hesitated. I gunned the motor. "Let's go, Shaw. Mr. Johnson will have my hide if we miss that plane."

"Yeah." Shaw climbed into the car and slammed the door. "Take it away."

Driving up U.S. 165 toward Columbia and Monroe I said, "I'm sure sorry to hear about your mother, Shaw. Like you, my mother is the only parent I have."

"I didn't know that." Shaw had been staring at the road ahead with a pale, stony expression on his face. He cleared his throat and his voice changed. "I haven't seen my mother for four years. I'm sorry about that now, but when my father was killed she got married again. To a stupid garage mechanic, Lester Chance. His idea of raising a kid was to clout him at least once a day, and use a belt on his backside. I still have the scars. When I was big enough I beat the tar out of him and ran away."

"How old were you?"

"Sixteen but I could pass as eighteen. I lived out of garbage cans and did a little stealing so I could hang around race tracks, begging for a ride. A car owner got so tired of me pestering him that he let me race a junk heap he didn't care about. I won the race and he gave me a better car. I kept winning because I had to."

"You've come along a rough road," I said.

Shaw shrugged. "Who has it easy? This All-Am series is my main chance. If I can make a good showing, I won't have to go around begging rides again, or teaching dunderheaded Sunday drivers how to race."

"We've got strong cars and the right backing," I told him. "You'll make it, all right."

"Yeah."

Shaw didn't speak again until we had reached Monroe. "None of what happened was Mother's fault," he said. "Dad was broke when he was killed and she had me to raise. So far as I know, Lester never laid a finger on her. He just didn't like having another man's kid around, and I guess I was a smart-ass."

"Is your stepfather still alive?"

"Sure. He somehow found out where I was and sent me that telegram. Collect, you might know."

When we had paid for his ticket, there was expense money left over for Shaw. "I judged Johnson as a big wheel with a cash register instead of a heart," Shaw said. Tears stood in his eyes. "I sure tagged him wrong."

"When you get back, join me at the Johnson estate," I told him. "Accommodations beat that sleazy motel, and the food is great."

"Yeah, I'll think about it," Shaw said.

Before I left Monroe I found a florist shop and

carried out the rest of the instructions relayed from Mr. Johnson by Kelly. I wired a wreath to the Los Angeles funeral home from which Shaw's mother would be buried.

At Dallas International a new team was added to the All-Am roster. A driver named Ron Cunningham, and a Frenchman, Pierre LaCroix, entered a pair of Datsun 240-Z sports coupes. These fast little cars (assembled in America to qualify for the series) had 146-cubic-inch displacement six-cylinder engines with overhead cams. They had been well prepared and went like a streak.

Cunningham, I learned, was an expatriate American who had inherited a meat fortune. He owned a villa on the French Riviera and his third wife was a titled Frenchwoman. Abroad he had been racing his own Lotus-Ford Formula 1 racers, Grand Prix cars with 5000 cubic centimeter engines in the rear.

Cunningham, LaCroix, and the Cunningham pit crew of Italians and Frenchmen, didn't mix with the rest of us. LaCroix was a small, swarthy man with a perpetual scowl who couldn't speak English. Off the track he sat alone in the bar drinking tall, thin glasses of some green liqueur.

Cunningham was a tall, spare man with a hawk-nosed face and ice-cold blue eyes. He didn't have so much as a nod for any of us. I remember him best for giving the bartender a hard time two nights before the race because the man didn't know how to mix some exotic drink that had absinthe in it.

84

Mark Owens had raced in Europe the past season, so I asked him about Cunningham. We were in Mark's pit area watching the blue-and-silver Datsuns flash past.

Mark almost invariably has something good to say about everyone, but Cunningham was the exception. Mark scowled at my question.

"Ron Cunningham has a high opinion of himself and his racing ability," Mark said, "but he's yet to win a major race. His best effort was a third at Le Mans two years ago, and that was a freak deal. A Ferrari went out of the race on the last lap. When Rene Dubois was killed in the Mille Miglia last year, some who saw Rene go into that ravine claim Cunningham crowded him off the road. There was an investigation, but nothing came of it."

"You don't like our friend, I take it."

"I don't know him personally. I'll admit the way he stalks around off the track as if he's a titled aristocrat and the rest of us are peasants gets under my skin."

"Why is he over here rubbing elbows with us peasants?" I asked. "I don't get it."

"Slumming, I suppose." Mark grinned. "Seeing how the other half lives." Mark now spoke seriously. "Cunningham is reckless as hell on the track, J.J. I've heard he eats pep pills by the handful before a race, but that's only rumor. Just the same, keep an eye peeled for him."

"Is LaCroix any good?" I asked.

"So-so," Mark said. "He was on the Ferrari team one season but they dropped him. I mark him down as a good journeyman driver, but no ball of fire."

"I've heard you're building a couple of Formula 1's to campaign Europe next season."

"You've heard right," Mark said. "Keep coming along as you have and I might want you to drive one of those cars."

After a dry winter, Texans had been praying for rain. The entire week before the race their prayers were answered. Rain came down in bucketfuls.

Dallas International isn't an easy circuit to drive. The start-finish is three quarters of the way down a long and wide dragstrip. You leave it going sharp right, run a section of track with a tricky bend in it, swing to the right again, then you're into a back "straight" that twists like a snake.

At the end of that section is the invariable 180-degree open hairpin inviting the careless driver to get out of shape. You slant from there back into the drag strip with a long, straight run to the start-finish. The track surface isn't as smooth as it should be.

All of us had to snatch our practice driving that week between rain squalls. That meant we were always driving on a wet track. Rain treads on the wheels helped, but none of us threatened to break any lap records.

Skies were overcast, but it only drizzled Saturday during qualification trials. If it rained Sunday, the race would be postponed a week. So Shaw and I turned in Saturday night, not knowing whether we would race the next day or not. We had qualified to

86

start side by side in the third row.

When Shaw had come back from Los Angeles, he had moved in with me at the Johnson estate. Now we were sharing a room at the Lone Star Motel. We also took our meals together.

Shaw still wasn't a talker, but I'm not much of a conversationalist myself, so we got along.

Sunday dawned bright and clear. By race time the thermometer read 99°. The track surface was half again as hot.

"Don't try to get up front the first half of this one," Kelly warned Shaw and me. "Let the other boys blow their engines and break their cars."

For some reason, all of us were nervous and strung out this race. Mark Owens, for instance, who had pole position, jumped the green flag. That meant the field had to be positioned again for another lap behind the pace car. That burns precious fuel and is hard on the nerves.

Once the race started, the first laps were as frantic as usual, with everyone jockeying for position. Shaw and I tried to stay cool and keep out of the way of overeager drivers. When Neal Hutchinson passed me, I latched onto his rear bumper to draft.

Mark Owens had the lead when the field began stringing out. Ace Allen and Walt Fischer, side by side, were behind him. Hutchinson and I were about six car lengths behind them. Shaw slotted in behind me to make it a three-car draft.

Red lights flashed on, stopping the race, but there hadn't been an accident on the track. Shaw and I pitted to top off our fuel tanks.

Kelly, Holcombe, and the pit crew were doubled over laughing.

"So what's so funny?" I asked Kelly. "We had a nice race going. Why have they stopped it?"

Kelly had to get his breath to tell me. "All the snakes in this part of Texas got out of the rain in the steward's booths," he said. "You never saw anything like it. The checkered-shirt down the track came yelling out of his booth with a six-foot diamondback latched on to his pants cuff."

"Like the one right behind you?" I asked.

Kelly jumped a foot in the air and nearly fell when he whirled around. There wasn't any snake, of course. That broke up the pit crew all over again.

It was half an hour before they had the snake situation under control and restarted the race.

Owens, Allen, and Fischer were running first, second, and third now. Hutchinson and I were fourth and fifth. Shaw was two car lengths behind me. All of us were being careful not to overdrive the track.

On one lap I noticed LaCroix was in the pits and out of his car. The hood was up.

On the next lap, going into the 180-degree turn, I saw Cunningham coming up. He crowded Shaw over the infield markers. If I hadn't braked just in time, he would have run me off the track too.

Coming out of the turn, Cunningham cut off Hutchinson. He had to stand on his brakes and fishtail his car to keep from rear-ending Cunningham.

Fischer and Allen saw Cunningham coming and

closed ranks. He was all over the track trying to pass them, but couldn't do it.

Down the drag strip Hutchinson, Shaw, and I went after Cunningham. We blew him off one, two, three, and Shaw cut him short. Bob Frazier and Gus Enright passed him on that lap too.

All of us, except Cunningham, were coming up to our first pit stop. His smaller engine, drinking less fuel, let him stay out longer.

With drivers slowing down to turn into pit alley, Cunningham should have been running wide down the drag strip. Instead, he came flat-out along the infield. I saw him and pulled sharp right to let him pass.

Ahead of me, Hutchinson saw Cunningham, too, and pulled right, as I had done, but by now the man evidently realized his mistake. He swung right too. Doing better than 150, he slammed into the side of Hutchinson's Mustang. The impact knocked Hutchinson's car 100 feet down the track, nearly slicing it in half.

Cunningham's Datsun squirted across the track and into the safety wall head on. His car folded like an accordion and burst into a tower of flame.

The fire engine skidded to a stop and firemen sprayed foam on Cunningham's blazing car, while two men in asbestos suits waded into the inferno to drag the man out.

Across the track, acetylene torches flickered as a rescue squad cut Neal Hutchinson out of his Mustang. Kelly and Holcombe helped drag the unconscious driver free. Ambulance attendants carefully loaded him onto a stretcher.

It was a sickening scene and I tasted bile in my throat. The crowd, everyone standing up, was hushed. The only sound from the packed grandstand was the muted screams of a hysterical woman, and a child crying.

The pits were silent as death.

Kelly and Holcombe joined us as soon as the ambulance spurted away. The grim look on their faces told the story, but I asked anyhow.

"How badly is Hutch hurt?" I said.

Kelly shook his head. "I think his back is broken."

"My God!" I crossed myself.

He wasn't Catholic but Shaw crossed himself, too. "Damn it all!" he said.

Cunningham in his smoldering driver's suit lay across the track in the classic "boxer's pose," knees drawn up and fists pressed to his chest. The attendants from the second ambulance were unfolding a plastic body bag.

Holcombe watched this with dead eyes. "Why did the screwball have to take a good man like Hutchinson with him?" he asked. He pounded a fist into the palm of his other hand. "Why?"

Before the race was restarted for the second time, we got the word in the pits. Neal Hutchinson died in the ambulance before it reached the hospital.

Shaw and I were buckling the chin straps of our helmets, getting ready to climb back into our cars. "How do you feel about racing now?" he asked me.

"I'd just as soon not try to answer that question," I told him.

"Yeah. Me, neither," Shaw said. "Why don't we shuck off these damned suits and quit?"

"Because we want to win this one."

8

I was nervous and shaky for a few laps after the race was restarted, but so were the other drivers. We made an effort to stay clear of one another and kept our speed down. Mark Owens shook off the dampening effect of the double accident first and began running away from us. Gus Enright and Jo Davidson in their Dodges tore out after him.

The rest of us weren't about to let this race go to Owens by default. I stopped seeing from the corner of my eye the blackened section of wall where Cunningham's car had burned and I got into a dice with Bruce Adams.

Shaw had Green Bird 31 somewhere behind me. Adams was low-point man in the series so far, but that was no reflection on his driving skill. We ran side by side, lap after lap, neither of us willing to back off.

Bob Frazier's Cutlass and Ace Allen's Camaro were behind us two car lengths. While trying to pull ahead of Allen, Frazier blew a front tire. In the rear-view I saw Shaw slice past his careening car, a beautiful piece of evasive driving.

Walt Fischer, trying to follow Shaw's example,

wasn't lucky. Frazier's car spun into his Chevy, and both of them were out of the race.

The heat inside my car was nearly unbearable, and leg cramps didn't help. I'd sucked the thermos lashed to the roll cage dry. The more I sweated the thirstier I got.

I redlined the tachometer down the drag strip in an all-or-nothing bid to pass Adams and establish myself in fourth place. The engine didn't lunch and Green Bird 13 held together. Adams made a game try to stay with me, but I beat him into the turn.

Davidson threw a rod. When he pitted I took over third place. Behind me, Adams was fighting off Shaw. Enright was ahead of me, Owens ahead of him.

Owens' Barracuda gained a few feet on Enright's Dodge each lap. Enright could stay with him along the straights, but Owens cornered faster. It was late in the race and time for me to make my bid.

I took on Enright. Shaw finally passed Adams and was on my rear bumper, setting up a draft. We passed Enright. Now only Owens stood between us and a one, two finish. But Shaw broke the draft, scraped me through a turn, and was running second.

Shaw wasn't about to let me draft along behind him.

"Well, if that's the way you want to drive this one," I muttered to myself, "let's find out who's the better driver."

I feinted to go over Shaw, then saw driving room and went under him, moving up to slam the gate in his face. He had to brake and almost lost his car. At that point, I wouldn't have cared if he had lost it and spun out.

I began nibbling away the distance separating me from Owens. To do it, I went deeper into turns than Owens went, braking later. Half the time my car was barely under control. But I was gaining and had forgotten all about Shaw.

Suddenly he was drafting Green Bird 31 on my rear bumper. Boosted along by the draft, we closed to within a car length of Owens going into the final lap. I knew we could now take Owens along the back straight.

Coming into the back straight, Shaw toed his brakes, broke the draft, and slingshotted past me. Shaw slammed into the 180-degree corner behind Owens but came out even with him.

Owens let him take the lead, drafted Shaw into the drag strip, then, opposite the pits, slingshotted *him!* Owens won by two seconds. Shaw came in second and I finished third. Gowanus had come on fast to nail down fourth place.

We had picked up 14 points and still led the series with 49. Mark Owens' Plymouths now had 40 points. The Fords had 34, the Oldsmobiles 28, the Chevs 24, and the Dodges 21.

Owens was still the top individual driver with 34 points, but I was runner-up with 28.

Chet Frazier had 19, Fischer 18, Gowanus 17, Davidson 16, Allen 14, Enright and Lockhart 14 points each. Adams was having a bad-luck season with only 8 points.

Shaw and I got a mixed reaction from Kelly and Mr. Johnson. Second money was $10,000, and third place paid $5,000. Teamwork could have netted us $15,000 and $10,000, or $25,000, so we'd blown away $10,000.

Mr. Johnson had every reason to be mad. If he was, he didn't let it show. He congratulated us first, then said, "These next three races, fellows, forget about beating each other."

Kelly was more blunt. "You made damned fools of yourselves out there," he told us. "Any more of that kind of racing and I'll find myself new drivers."

"I race to win," Shaw argued. "Justin can take care of himself."

"Yes, and it ain't his fault he didn't take care of you," Kelly pointed out. "It was a stupid exhibition."

Back at the motel, packing to leave, Shaw and I had nothing to say to each other. The wall of silence stayed up during the long night of driving back through Texas and Louisiana to Johnsonville. Both of us were dead-tired, haunted by the fatal accident, and sore at each other.

Mrs. Keller had a late breakfast on the table when we finally reached the Johnson estate. Dee wanted to hear about the race, but neither of us would talk.

"Okay, guys," she said, throwing up her hands. "Don't tell me about it. Who cares?"

When she left us alone, Shaw and I stared at each other. "We're being stupid about this thing," I said. "You made a mistake and I compounded the error. I could have made you pile up and I didn't care much one way or the other at the time. That's being really dumb."

Shaw managed one of his rare grins. "We gave first place to Owens. Let's not do it again."

"You've got a deal," I told him. "Let's not try to outsmart each other at Donnybrooke."

We had two weeks before the 250-mile race at Donnybrooke Speedway near Brainerd, Minnesota, in the lake country 140 miles west of Minneapolis and St. Paul. I had finished at Dallas International barely able to get out of my car unassisted. More than 2200 miles of racing since March was taking its toll.

My nerves were jumpy, I wasn't sleeping well, and my appetite wasn't good. It was a physical and mental effort to test drive Green Bird 13. I was absentminded in the shop. Everyone there got on my nerves, even Kelly, and once I threw a wrench across the shop when I barked my knuckles tightening a nut.

Everyone stopped working to stare at me.

Kelly stopped, picked up the wrench, and ambled over to where I was standing. With his head he motioned for me to join him in his office.

"Sit down, J.J." He laid the wrench on his littered desk and kicked the door shut. "Ain't you a little stale and nervy?"

I wiped a hand across my face. "I guess I am. I haven't had a tantrum like that since I was a kid."

"Go somewhere and forget about racing next week," Kelly said. "You've earned a rest. Go take it."

I spent the weekend and the first three days of next week in Columbia, getting acquainted with my mother again. Thursday, Shaw and I would fly up to Minneapolis and rent a car to reach Brainerd. We would fly to the rest of the races. Joe Holcombe and his crew would stay with the team for the windup of the series. Kelly and Mr. Johnson wanted Shaw and me rested and fresh when it was race time.

I found myself something of a local celebrity. Everyone I met on the street wanted me to talk about my racing experiences. I couldn't even walk over to the post office without being stopped three or four times.

I was most frequently asked about the accident at Dallas International that killed Neal Hutchinson and Ron Cunningham.

"How did a terrible thing like that happen?" someone would say.

I found my best answer was, "It was just one of those things. People get killed out on the highway too."

I didn't try to explain that Cunningham had downed a handful of pills before the race, and, if he hadn't been killed, would have been barred from car racing in this country for life.

"I'm supposed to be taking a vacation from racing," I told Mother at breakfast Wednesday morning, "but that's all anyone wants to talk with me about. It gets tiresome."

"What do you expect?" Mother asked. "Car racing has a certain glamour. You're doing something different. You'd be disappointed if people weren't interested in your career."

"I suppose I would be," I admitted, "but you can't explain what it's like on the track. You can't tell them if there wasn't money in it, you'd still be out there racing. I think most people around here consider me some kind of speed freak. They all wish me luck, but their eyes measure me for a coffin."

Mother finished her coffee. "Tell me one thing, James." She carefully put her cup back in the saucer, not looking directly at me. "Will you be satisfied with a racing career a year from now, or, say, five years from now?"

"How can I know the answer to that question?" I asked. "Right now I like racing. There's a chance I might go to Europe next season to drive one of Mark Owens' Formula 1 racers. I sure wouldn't want to miss that."

"Of course you wouldn't," Mother said, "and at twenty-two it's your life to live. Working offshore, I suppose, is nearly as dangerous as driving a race car."

"Maybe more dangerous. It's harder work, I'll tell you that."

"Maybe it doesn't mean much to you now, but we all get older. How many men over forty are still racing?"

"Darned few. Accidents, fatal or otherwise, retire quite a few drivers. When you've turned forty, your reflexes slow down, and you lose some of your competitive edge, or so Kelly tells me."

"It's too bad we couldn't send you to college,"

Mother said. "If you had gone, what would have been your major?"

"I don't know. I suppose I'd have taken a general course until I found something I wanted to do. Engineering, maybe. Math was one of my best subjects. Now, however, I know what I'd choose as a major."

"And what would that be?" Mother asked.

"Automotive engineering."

"Strange," Mother said. "Just the other evening, Dennis Johnson said you'd do well to take some courses in automotive engineering. He seems to hold you in high regard."

"When did you see Dennis?" I asked. "He's back at Tulane now."

"I was referring to Dennis Johnson, Sr.," Mother said.

"Oh?"

"Yes." Mother didn't elaborate.

When I met Shaw at Selman Field in Monroe to fly up to Minneapolis, I was rested, relaxed, and ready to race again. We left Thursday noon, changed planes in Chicago, and were in Minneapolis late that afternoon. We rented a car at the airport to drive to Brainerd, where we had a reservation at the Lac Mille Lacs Motel.

We would practice Friday, qualify Saturday, and race Sunday. Donnybrooke would be our last race before heading for the West Coast.

"Flying beats towing that trailer," I told Shaw after we had registered. "The only thing better would be if Mr. Johnson bought a Lear jet and hired a pilot and copilot. Then we could make these races in style, like Mark Owens does."

"If we had his kind of money, we could buy us a 747 complete with hostesses," Shaw said. "I wonder how it feels to be as rich as he is? If I was, damned if I'd risk my life racing."

Donnybrooke is a three-mile circuit opened in 1968. Lap record, before we All-Am drivers arrived, was 120 mph set by Denis Hulme. It's a fast circuit with long straights and no problem corners.

Ford had replaced Hutchinson's Mustang with a Galaxie and hired Burke Wallace, an Australian, to drive it. The Galaxie had the big 460-cube mill. Burke "Down Under" had impressive wins in his own country as well as in Tasmania and South Africa.

Chevrolet replaced Walt Fischer's Monte Carlo with a Camaro identical to Ace Allen's. So we had one new driver and two new cars in the Donnybrooke race.

Shaw and I were the last All-Am drivers to check in. An accessory manufacturer was sponsoring a cocktail party. Jo Davidson corraled us before we got to our room.

"Hey, fellows, come on." Jo obviously had downed a few drinks. "We're drowning Dallas and drinking to Donnybrooke. Where have you been? You've got some catching up to do."

"We haven't unpacked, Jo," I said. "Anyway, we have to drive tomorrow."

"Who doesn't? Toss your luggage in your room and come along."

"I could stand a beer," Shaw said.

The other drivers had a good headstart, there was no doubt about that. Burke Wallace had an Aussie campaign hat cocked on the side of his blond head and was rendering "Waltzing Matilda" in a better than average baritone. Bud Gowanus was playing the piano.

Bruce Adams, Walt Fischer, and Bob Frazier were having a heated discussion about a race last season, who won and who should have won, but they weren't getting anywhere because each was talking about a different race.

Gus Enright and Ace Allen sat at a table arm wrestling. The rest of the drivers were harrying two red-coated bartenders.

Mark Owens sat in a chair slanted against the wall nursing a drink. There was an amused expression on his face.

I followed Shaw's suit and settled for a tall glass of draft beer. Mark beckoned us over.

"Cheers." Mark raised his glass when we joined him. "Look at this drive hard, play hard bunch," he said. "The pressure is getting to them. There will be a drain on the oxygen tanks tomorrow morning, sure enough."

"Where's our host?" I asked.

"Sleeping it off in the bedroom," Mark said. "They

101

should issue these factory reps plastic stomachs. There's no way you can drink a race driver under the table."

"How are your Formula 1 cars shaping up?" I asked.

"Just great. I test drove the first one yesterday. You'll have to drive it to believe . . . Oh, oh."

Kelly had arrived.

"We were just about to look you up," I said.

We had finished our beer. Kelly took the empty glasses. "In a pig's eye you were," he said. "This bash will go on all night. I want you two at the track in condition to drive at six tomorrow morning, so it's beddy-bye."

Mark chuckled. "Ride herd on 'em, Kelly."

"I'll hog-tie 'em if I have to," Kelly said.

Shaw and I liked the Donnybrooke track. It was smooth and it took only a few laps to find our best driving line. After that we cut 115 to 118 mph laps with no trouble. We had the track to ourselves, except for Mark Owens, until other drivers began straggling into the pits after nine o'clock.

Unofficially we had both broken Hulme's record by the end of the day. Kelly clocked Shaw around at 121. My best lap was 122.

"Which doesn't mean much," Kelly said, after he had told us. "Both the Camaros and the Fords have been cutting faster laps. Mark Owens has set up his cars differently for this race. They're faster than ever. To win or place here, you fellows will really have to charge. And none of this Dallas funny business."

Bruce Adams established an official new track record when he qualified at 126 mph. That cinched pole position for him.

I was quick qualifying, or so I thought, but other drivers bumped me back into the fourth row on the starting grid.

Shaw had bad luck. A cracked sparkplug kept his speed down. He wound up outside in the last row. Burke Wallace was back there with him.

When we were getting ready to go to bed that night, Shaw said, "We're really going to have to put it all together to win tomorrow."

"You'd better believe," I said.

The Camaros were red-hot. Wallace snaked up through the field early in the race, pushing his Galaxie hard, and joined his teammate, Gowanus, to challenge Allen and Fischer for the lead.

Adams was pounding along right behind Wallace and Gowanus. Plymouth strategy was for Owens to stay just off the pace, taking command if Adams ran into trouble.

Speaking of trouble, after only twelve laps, the engine sound of Green Bird 13 changed. Revs were up, the engine wasn't overheating, oil and fuel pressures were okay. I decided something was wrong with my ears until a connecting rod let go.

With the engine now sounding like a washing machine I coasted into pit alley, but not before the crankshaft snapped.

"Here's your car back," I told Kelly. "All it needs is a new engine. Got one in your pocket?"

Kelly popped the hood, inspecting the damage, hands on his hips, then said, "You're very funny, J.J."

I tried to console him. "Shaw's still going."

I squeezed between Joe Holcombe and Billy Welch on the pit wall to watch the race. Shaw was driving a magnificent race. He passed Wallace, and then Adams. Shaw was hot after Allen and Fischer when he hit an oil slick, probably the one I'd laid down coming in.

Sideways, his car slid up to shower sparks off the wall protecting the grandstand. That put him into a looping spin back across the track, but he somehow got his car under control.

No sooner was Shaw straightened out than Adams' Barracuda tail ended him. Adams bent his bumper and radiator protection grill but kept racing.

The rear end of Green Bird 31 was torn up and Shaw had a nasty whiplash. He lapped around and came into the pits. I had to help him out of the car.

"We should have stayed in Johnsonville!" Kelly groaned.

9

When I came back from escorting Shaw to the track hospital, Kelly was haggling with a tech inspector and Holcombe was burning off chunks of loose sheet metal. Kelly prevailed and the inspector said we could continue racing the car.

"All right, take it out, J.J.," Kelly said. "We can at least get one car across the start-finish line."

The suspension was wracked. Vibration had my teeth popping and Green Bird 31 wallowed through the turns. Slow or fast, the vibration was the same, so I speeded up and fought my way through turns.

I stayed dead-last the rest of the race but did manage to finish.

Every muscle in my body was sore when I got out of the car, and I had a fierce headache. "Now that's what I call earning one point the hard way," I told Kelly.

"One point can win this series," he reminded me.

Allen and Fischer finished their Camaros one, two. Wallace took third place, and Gowanus came in fourth.

The Fords now led the series with 52 points to our

50. Mark Owens' Plymouth team had 42 points, the Chevrolets 34, the Dodges 23. The Oldsmobiles 30.

Owens was the leading individual driver with 35 points, but I had 29. Fischer had 26, Allen 24, Gowanus 21, Chet Frazier 20, Davidson 17, Bob Frazier 17, Lockhart 14, Adams 9, and Wallace 6.

In August we would race 250 miles at Laguna Seca. Ontario had finally been chosen for the last 500-mile race, and we would go on the superspeedway there.

Any team could still win the series, the cup, and $350,000. And only a few drivers were out of the running for the $150,000 to be awarded the individual with the most points.

Pressure was really building. Our luck would have to change.

We raced at Donnybrooke July 15. The 250-mile Laguna Seca race would be August 14, the 500-miler at Ontario August 31.

When our cars were back in the shop, the engine I had blown had to be replaced. More serious, however, was the problem of Green Bird 31. After Shaw's brush with the wall, the rear-end collision damage was more extensive than we had thought. Not only had suspension been damaged but the car's frame was bent.

"We can fix the frame," Kelly told Mr. Johnson, "but I can't guarantee it will stand up for another 750 miles of racing. To play it safe, we need a new car."

We had spent more money than Mr. Johnson had

budgeted for racing and had lost the lead in the series, but he was game.

"I'll see what sort of deal I can make with the factory," Mr. Johnson promised. "They should be keen for us to get back on top. I understand Ford's racing division is gloating."

Mr. Johnson reported back to Kelly, "We've got a choice. Detroit will ship us a Firebird off their assembly line, or we can buy a Grand Prix prepared to race."

Shaw was in Johnsonville General Hospital, being treated for the whiplash he got in Minnesota, so Kelly and I discussed the matter.

"The Grand Prix is four and a half inches longer, four and nine tenths inches wider, and two and a half inches higher than a Firebird," he told me, "but, most important, it's heavier and has eight inches more wheelbase. That's going to affect car-handling."

"Who prepared the Grand Prix?"

"Old friends of mine, Ralph Jarrett and Bill Jordan in their Winston-Salem factory. I've had Ralph on the phone. We'll have some work to do on it, but basically it's a sound racing car. They've been getting it ready for Smokey Phillips to use next season on the NASCAR circuit."

"Next question," I said. "Have we time to prepare a production Firebird?"

Kelly ran a hand through his hair. "If we have to, yes, but we're short of time. We couldn't do a really careful job and give you or Shaw a chance to learn the car before the Laguna Seca race."

"Is the engine a 455-cube?"

Kelly nodded. "Which way do you think we ought to go, J.J.?"

"Take the Grand Prix."

Kelly was thoughtful. "I'll have to talk with Mr. Johnson, but I'm inclined to agree."

I was too familiar with Green Bird 13 to want the new car. The 1.9 asphalt Laguna Seca short circuit would be challenge enough for me without racing unfamiliar machinery. I thought Shaw, with more experience behind him, would want the Grand Prix.

When Kelly told me we were taking delivery on the Jarrett-Jordan prepared car, I asked, "Who's going to drive it?"

"You and Shaw decide," Kelly said.

I visited Shaw in the hospital. He was pale under his tan and still in pain. I explained the situation.

"Do you or I drive the Grand Prix?" I asked.

"I'll take Green Bird 13." Shaw hadn't hesitated before answering.

When I told him about Shaw's decision, Kelly laughed. "It figures he'd grab your car. Shaw is too win-hungry to take a chance in the Grand Prix."

Two days later the GP arrived in Johnsonville. When it was repainted and numbered 31, we took it over to Georgetown. I did the test driving on the road circuit.

The longer wheelbase made an amazing difference in car-handling, especially on the turns. The right line for Green Bird 13 was wrong for GP 31.

Car weight was another factor. There was more brake wear, and it felt sluggish accelerating along the straights. Installation of a turbo supercharger gave me better acceleration, but I still didn't believe the car was as quick as Green Bird 13.

The Green Birds had manual steering. GP 31 had power steering. I had some bad moments on the track before I adjusted to that.

The GP31 gearbox was a four-speed racing turbo hydramatic. Kelly was skeptical about this, afraid it might blow up while racing, but I liked it. Without having to use the clutch I could concentrate better on steering.

It took a week of hard driving to get the GP where its performance satisfied both Kelly and me, but by that time I liked the car.

Shaw came out of a week's bed rest ready to drive Green Bird 13 and the layoff hadn't hurt his driving edge.

When two drivers practice on the same track, sooner or later they'll try to find out who's the faster. Shaw and I had our match race two days before the cars were loaded into the van for the long tow to California.

I was passing him down the main straight when Shaw decided he didn't want to be blown off.

For a dozen fast laps it was anyone's race. The shorter wheelbase made Shaw a bit more nimble through the turns, but I could always catch him along the straights. Kelly finally waved us in off the track.

"Either one of you prove anything?" he asked. "Let's not take any chances and scatter these cars."

Laguna Seca is a 30-foot wide, hilly track, 700 feet above sea level in the pit area, and 940 feet at its highest point. It's on the Fort Ord Army Base outside Monterey, the colorful old Spanish capital of California.

The Sports Car Racing Association of Monterey Peninsula (SCRAMP) leases the track, and all profits are given to charity.

From the start-finish you race through a banked left turn into a short straight, sweep through a left-hand bend, drive another straight, go through another bend. From there you drive into a hairpin turn left, immediately followed by a hairpin right.

If you're still on the track after those tire scrubbers, a sweeper left, a straight, then a sharp left turn leads you back into the main straight.

It takes a lot of steering, shifting, and braking to get around this one. The hills, also, are a problem. You can't see what's happening ahead. That's hard on the nervous system.

Suspension is tricky too. If it's too loose, the car body tries to leave the chassis when you top a hill. Tighten it too much to overcome this roller-coaster effect and all four tires may leave the track when you come over a hill. It was a day and a half before we had both cars set up right.

Lap record at Laguna Seca, before we All-Am drivers began shooting at it, was 109 mph, established by Denis Hulme in the same McClaren-Chevrolet he drove at Donnybrooke.

In practice I was lapping consistently at 107 to 108 mph. Shaw was coming around in about the same speed range. Both of us knew we could be quicker.

Bruce Adams had won at Laguna Seca twice before. Mark Owens had won a Canadian-American Cup race here. Bruce qualified at 112 mph, setting a new lap record, which Mark immediately broke. He averaged 114 mph around the course.

Shaw drove a 115 lap. I surprised myself by qualifying at 114.5 mph. That gave him pole position with me sitting beside him. We were favored to win.

We wanted to win at Laguna Seca and get the lead back from the Fords so badly it hurt!

Sunday was a clear, warm day with enough ocean breeze to make it comfortable, but not enough to blow the cars around.

Shaw and I got away fast. Bruce Adams, Burke Wallace, Mark Owens, and Walt Fischer, in that order, chased us, with the rest of the field bunched behind them.

Shaw would take the lead one lap, and I'd get it back the next time around. We drove like that for the first 50 miles.

Suddenly something shattered my windshield. Blood and feathers covered my face shield, half blinding me. I swerved all over the track. The slipstream through the hole in my windshield stirred up a cloud of dust and grit in the car.

111

I drove across the first hairpin and skidded down the short road put there as a safety valve for drivers who can't make it around. I wiped an arm across my face shield. Looking behind me, I found what was left of the sea gull that had dive-bombed me.

When I was turned around, and the track was clear (Shaw was still leading), I pulled out and drove into the pits.

Kelly thought I had overdriven the hairpin. "What the hell?" he began, then saw the hole in my car's windshield. "What happened? Are you hurt?"

Billy Welch was slapping a duct tape patch over the hole.

"It's not my blood," I told Kelly. I pointed to the mangled bird. "Can you get it out of here for a decent burial?"

A tech inspector had loped over. None of the cracks in the windshield interfered with my vision.

"You can stay in the race," he told Kelly.

Back on the track, I was two full laps behind the nearest car. I'm not ashamed of the Laguna Seca race. Determined not to finish last again, I let it all hang out. By the 200-mile mark I'd passed Jo Davidson, Bob Frazier, and Walt Fischer.

Ace Allen's Camaro pitted with ignition trouble and didn't come out again. That advanced me from seventh to sixth place.

Adams and Owens were keeping Shaw honest. Adams got ahead of him for four laps. Shaw got the lead back, but Owens came on, flat-out, and took it away from him for three laps.

Shaw finally outdrove Owens.

Bud Gowanus blew his Cougar's engine trying to catch the leaders and was DNF. That put me in fifth place behind Wallace's Galaxie.

I stormed after Wallace, but the crafty Australian pulled out all the stops to hold me back. He shifted to my line through the corners and always kept a piece of his car in my way.

Shaw held off both Adams and Owens, driving a slam-bang final lap. Adams had to settle for second, Owens for third place, Wallace for fourth. I came in only one second behind Wallace.

After the race I wanted to tell Burke what I thought of his driving, but the big guy's easy smile disarmed me. "Wash down the dust, mate," he said, and handed me a cold can of beer. "You had me worried out there, and I don't worry easy."

I thanked him for the beer.

With 61 points we led the series again. Mark Owens' Plymouths had earned 56, and the Fords 56.

The Chevrolets had 35, the Oldsmobiles 32, and the Dodges 25.

Owens had 41 individual points. I had 30, Fischer 27, Lockhart 24, Chet Frazier 21, Bob Frazier and Davidson 18, Adams 17, Enright 14, and Wallace 10.

Our team, the Owens Plymouths, and the Fords would be driving to win the All-Am Championship and $350,000 at Ontario. The Camaros, the Cutlasses, and the Challengers were out of the running.

Mark Owens had won $150,000 at Laguna Seca.

None of us could catch up with him at Ontario. A win there would leave me still a point shy.

"Them that has, gets," Shaw commented about that. "Mark needs more scratch like I need another head."

Kelly, Holcombe and his crew, as well as Shaw, stayed in California after Laguna Seca to get ready for the Ontario 500. Shaw also had personal business to attend to after the death of his mother. I would fly back to rejoin Shaw three days before the race.

Mark Owens offered me a lift to Johnsonville in his personal plane. "I can land on the strip there," he told me, "and it won't be out of my way. Rumors are around that Dennis Johnson is building a European plant near Paris. I should be able to persuade him to foot part of the bill for campaigning my Formula 1's next season. He can use the advertising exposure."

Mark had a copilot aboard, but he took the Lear jet off the ground himself and flew it for half an hour. Coming back into the cabin, he eased himself into the seat next to mine.

"What are your plans for next season, Jim?"

"So far I haven't any. If there's a second All-Am series, and he wants me, I'll probably drive for Mr. Johnson. That's up in the air, of course."

"I ask because you're getting pretty good in a race car," Mark said. "I need a driver for my second Formula 1. Would you be interested?"

"I sure enough would be."

"The circuits are more dangerous over there," Mark warned me. "You'll be racing the world's best Formula 1 drivers, too. Do you think you can hack it?"

"I'd like a chance to try, Mark."

He grinned. "You've got it. When we're through in Ontario, we'll fly back East. You can help me build and test the cars."

Before Mark left Johnsonville, Mr. Johnson had a poolside barbecue in his honor. They had reached a sponsorship agreement.

Dennis came up from Tulane to escort Voncil. Mother was there as Mr. Johnson's guest. They were, I noticed, on a warm, first-name basis.

Dee brought a gawky boyfriend, whose name I can't remember, and the most attractive woman I had ever seen. She was tall and filled a swimsuit that was more interesting than a bikini.

She had a smooth olive complexion, wore her wavy black hair long, and had dark-brown eyes almost too large for her face.

There are girls, and then there are women, but this one was special. I stood beside the diving board in my swim trunks and stared at her. It wasn't polite, but I couldn't help it.

When Dee had introduced her to Dennis, Voncil, Mr. Johnson, Mark, and my mother, up at the opposite end of the pool, they came along the side of the pool to where I was standing.

"I want you to meet my math teacher, J.J.," Dee said in a subdued voice.

"Miss Hardscrabble?" I said it without thinking.

Dee blushed deep red. "No, you goose, Miss Burkitt, Sonia Burkitt."

Dee fled and left us standing there.

Sonia's lips were pressed together, and she was having trouble with her facial expression, but I couldn't tell whether she was angry or trying not to laugh at me.

I finally realized she was holding out a slender hand for me to shake, so I took it.

"I'm glad to meet you, Sonia."

"I'm glad to meet you, too, James," she said. "You certainly improved Dee's math homework, but I doubt that you added much to her grasp of math. I don't advise you to choose teaching as a career."

"I don't have it in mind," I said. "Car racing is more my speed. Shall we swim?"

"Let's."

I gave her a hand up on the diving board. She proceeded to cleave the water in a near-perfect swan dive.

I tried a jackknife. It didn't come off. I hit the water flat.

Sonia broke up laughing. "You'd better stay with racing," she said, "because you'll never make the next Olympics as a diver."

Treading water beside her, I asked, "You're not engaged, married, or something like that, are you?"

116

"It so happens I'm not," Sonia said, "but do you always ask such personal questions?"

"Race you to the other end of the pool," I said to change the subject.

10

Sonia's home was in Lafayette in the southern part of Louisiana, and she had done her undergraduate work at Louisiana State University in Baton Rouge. This summer she was taking courses toward her Master's over at Northeastern. She shared an apartment with an older teacher in Johnsonville.

For me time was short. I had only a few days before I had to fly to California for the Ontario 500. I'll guarantee I made the most of what time I had.

Sonia and I swam in the Johnson pool. We rode horses and twice had dinner and spent the evening in Monroe. She was the first girl I ever took to meet my mother.

The night before I was to fly to Los Angeles, Mrs. Keller fixed us supper and afterward we took a moonlight swim in the pool. It was one of those warm southern summer nights, scented with wisteria and magnolia blossoms, when stars seem close enough to touch.

Tired of swimming, we sat on the edge of the pool kicking our feet in the water. My arm was around her

118

waist. Sonia's lips were cool but faintly responsive when I kissed her.

"I don't understand it," I said. "I can talk a blue streak to other girls. Around you, most of the time I'm tongue-tied."

Sonia smiled. "You do all right, Jim. Is there anything special you wanted to talk with me about? I'm a good listener."

"Yes. I want to talk about you and me."

"Go ahead." Sonia was staring up at the stars. Star points were reflected in her eyes.

"You have a good profile," I said, "but it doesn't tell me much."

Sonia's dark eyes met mine. "Is this better?"

"Much better. I'm in love with you, Sonia."

"I've come to realize that, Jim." Sonia frowned at me. "Let's assume I feel the same way toward you. Where does that leave us?"

"We could do something about it, like get married."

"Let's look logically at what's between us," Sonia said. "It's habit with me to think in mathematical terms. We have an equation here, A plus B. A is a race driver, while B is a schoolteacher. To balance our equation, A plus B equals X. X is the unknown factor, of course."

"What you need is a piece of chalk and a blackboard," I said.

Sonia laughed. "I'll ignore that. There are two possible answers to this equation. X equals a happy life

119

for A and B, or X equals incompatibility, unhappiness, and possibly divorce, although divorce for us would be out of the question, wouldn't it?"

"Since we share the same religious beliefs, yes. I like your first answer. I think it's the right one."

"You can give me love, Jim. I know that, but it isn't enough. A woman wants security, too, at least a woman like me does. Can you give me that?"

"I don't know, and that's an honest answer. I'll be racing in Europe next season. We could make a honeymoon out of it."

"Between races, of course. I've always wanted to see Europe, but not at the price of becoming a young widow."

"I could quit racing."

"You don't mean that, Jim, and it's too much for me to ask. If you really did quit, you'd blame me and hate me. Racing is your life."

"Why the devil," I said, "do I have to fall in love with an intelligent woman? Look, can we leave it now, and talk after the Ontario 500?"

"Of course."

Finished in 1970, Ontario Motor Speedway is a three-mile oval, similar to The Brickyard in Indianapolis, but with 90-degree banked turns, which make it a faster track.

I joined Shaw at the Ontario Motor Hotel near the speedway a few days before the race. He had checked in a day ahead of me and had spent it practice driving, so I asked, "How do you like this track?"

"I've always liked it," he told me. "I was a driving instructor on the road course here. I've also raced on the superspeedway twice. For me, this is homecoming."

"Then you should be able to give me some driving tips. A first place here wins the series for us."

"The best tip I can give you is stay alive," Shaw said. "By the way, I want to drive GP 31 if you don't object. Kelly's leaving it up to you."

"I like the new car now," I told him.

"I'm partial to it myself," Shaw said. "Shall we flip a coin?"

"Go ahead. I'll call it heads."

"My lucky coin." Shaw had a silver dollar in his hand, an old one with the eagle on it. "Do you have any objections?"

"No. A coin is a coin."

Shaw flipped and it came up tails. I'd be racing Green Bird 13 again.

Ontario awed me the first few times I lapped around the track. Come Sunday, 180,000 people would pack those towering grandstands that now cast black shadows across the track. The final All-Am race was a sellout.

Forty thousand was first money. That kept the Chevys, Oldsmobiles, and Dodges still racing, although they were out of contention for the $350,000 jackpot.

Ontario's oval reminded me of Texas International, the only other time we had raced a superspeedway, and Phil Spell burning to death in his car was fresh in my mind.

Shaw drove as if he owned Ontario. He turned 180 to 185 laps in GP 31 consistently, while I drove Green Bird 13 conservatively. I couldn't achieve the mood of total concentration I would need during the race. On the track, as well as off it, Sonia was on my mind.

And I was experiencing something else I'd never contended with before. I had a gut-feeling that's hard to describe that my luck might be running out. I had had my share of close shaves in previous All-Am races, but I hadn't been hurt yet. But at the speeds we'd be traveling here at Ontario, my mistake or someone else's could put me in the hospital or, God forbid! the morgue.

I'll say it bluntly—I was scared.

Kelly sensed this. He took me aside Friday afternoon before qualifying trials.

"How do you feel about this race, J.J.?"

"Right now, Kelly?"

He nodded.

"I wish I was somewhere else. I'll shake down tomorrow, though, and be ready to win or know the reason why not Sunday. Don't worry about me."

"Don't worry? Hell, I worry about anyone out there in a car I've prepared. A loose nut or cross-threaded bolt can cost him his life. That's a lot of responsibility for a man to carry, you know?"

"I guess it is. I've never looked at it that way."

Kelly wasn't satisfied. "Forget the money and prestige at stake in Sunday's race," he told me. "I've seen good drivers hang it up in the middle of a big race just because they no longer felt right on the track. If you get that feeling, come in. We'll say something was wrong with the car."

"Don't worry about me," I said again. "I'll be all right tomorrow and Sunday."

I was all right Saturday when I qualified at 190 mph, fast enough to put Green Bird 13 on the pole. Mr. Johnson and Kelly were delighted.

Mark Owens qualified at 189 mph and would sit beside me on the starting grid. Shaw and Bruce Adams were right behind us.

This is Sunday morning. Shaw has left for the track and I've been to early Mass. After Mass I phoned Sonia. That might have been a mistake.

Neither of us had much to say. The race will be on national television and I asked if she was going to watch it.

"No, Jim," she said, "but good luck."

Time to leave for the track.

Mark Owens reporting:

Jim Justin's mother, now Mrs. Dennis Johnson, has asked me to write this epitaph to Jim's racing career.

Bruce Adams and I knew that to win the series we had to beat Shaw and Jim, as well as the Wallace and Gowanus Fords. We had installed new engines. Our cars were perfectly tuned for the Ontario track. Bruce and I planned to dominate the race from start to finish.

"Shaw won't spare you an inch of driving room on the track," Bruce remarked before the race. "In that Grand Prix he's the driver to beat."

I didn't tell Bruce, but I was worried about Jim. Early in the series I'd spotted him as a comer, a driver with the potential to be great. I'd seen him improve, race after race. Back in Green Bird 13 he would be hard to beat.

When we got the starting flag and had raced a few laps, Wallace and Gowanus were crowding Bruce and me for the lead. Driving against them, I forgot Jim.

Shaw pitted early when the Grand Prix's turbo hydramatic transmission packed in.

It was a mistake to forget Jim Justin. We had gone 300 miles when I caught a flash of green out of the corner of my eye. Jim was streaking along the guardrail coming into the top turn.

He'll never make it, I thought.

Jim not only made it through the turn, but he passed *all four* of us leaders.

At the speed he was going we expected Jim to blow his car. We didn't know it, but that was the race for the rest of us. Bruce and I tried, Wallace and Gowanus tried, but Jim's driving was flawless. We couldn't catch up with Green Bird 13, much less pass Jim.

One lap they clocked Jim at 215 mph along the back straight.

Jim got the checkered flag 15 seconds ahead of me and 20 seconds ahead of Bruce, and 23 seconds ahead of Gowanus. Jim's 10 points brought the Johnson Pontiac team a total of 71. My second place and Bruce's third netted us 70 points.

After crossing the start-finish, and before I could turn an extra lap and pit, my car died with a cracked distributor head. It was parked squarely in the middle of the track.

Bruce parked his Barracuda up the track and came back to help me. Our pit crew was out there, too, while Jim idled around his extra lap.

I glanced over my shoulder. Jim was coming out of the top turn slowly.

"Let's move this junker," I told Bruce and my pit crew. "We'll block Jim out of Victory Circle."

My back was turned, but I heard the roar of Jim's engine as it raced from idle to wide-open, hurtling his green car right at us. For a moment I thought he had flipped out, then realized his throttle linkage had snapped.

Spectators screamed.

Clustered around my dead car, Bruce, our pit crew, and I froze.

Jim stood on his brakes, knocked his car out of gear, and cut the switch, but Green Bird 13 had too much momentum. It came at us like a juggernaut. We didn't have a chance.

Jim had unbuckled while turning his extra lap, and dropped his helmet in the bottom of the car, so I had a clear view of his face just before he threw the steering wheel over to ram head on into the concrete safety wall.

There was no fear on his face.